INSIDER'S GUIDE TO TEACHING WITH THE TRIOLA STATISTICS SERIES

The Triola Statistics Series:

Elementary Statistics, Tenth Edition

Elementary Statistics Using Excel, Third Edition

Essentials of Statistics, Third Edition

Elementary Statistics Using the Graphing Calculator, Second Edition

Mario F. Triola

Dutchess Community College

Boston San Francisco New York
London Toronto Sydney Tokyo Singapore Madrid
Mexico City Munich Paris Cape Town Hong Kong Montreal

Reproduced by Pearson Addison-Wesley from electronic files supplied by the author.

Publishing as Pearson Addison-Wesley, 75 Arlington Street, Boston, MA 02116

ISBN 0-321-40964-7

2 3 4 5 6 BB 08 07

Contents

I. *Introduction*

Dear Professor:

The Triola/Addison-Wesley team is delighted that you are using a book in the Triola statistics series. The author has personally visited many professors across the United States, and he is happy to see a wide range of extremely effective statistics courses. Some professors have many years of productive experience, and they continue to improve their courses each year. Other professors are relatively new to teaching statistics. Some professors are adjuncts who do not teach on a full-time basis, and their contact with other teachers is minimal. In some cases, large sections are taught with teaching assistants who might be graduate students with little or no teaching experience. This *Insider's Guide to Teaching Statistics* is intended to provide some insight into effective teaching for all of these groups.

Please know that the recommendations and suggestions in this guide are not being made in an authoritarian spirit of "you *must* do it *this* way." The content of this guide should be tempered with personal teaching styles, individual course objectives, and individual student needs and goals.

In addition to teaching students fundamental concepts of statistics, the introductory statistics course is an excellent vehicle for doing much more than teaching course content. We have a course that provides us with an ideal opportunity to foster student growth in these important areas:

Critical thinking

Technology usage

Public speaking

Working cooperatively in groups

This guide includes recommendations that are helpful in encouraging student growth in these important areas.

We hope that this guide is helpful, and any suggestions for improvement are most welcome. We sincerely wish you the best of luck!

II. How should statistics be taught?

One of the most important points to be made in this *Insider's Guide* is the basic approach to teaching the introductory statistics course. Here are some important principles:

1. The introductory statistics course should be taught in a way that is fundamentally different from the approach used in traditional mathematics courses. The arithmetic computations are not nearly as important as the ability to *understand* results and to be able to *interpret* results in a meaningful way.
2. The introductory statistics course focuses on real applications instead of abstractions.
3. Books in the Triola statistics series are full of real data. Examples, exercises, and test questions should involve students with real data as much as possible. Fabricated data have little or no use in the introductory statistics course.
4. There should not be a high priority placed on covering as many different topics as possible. It is much better to cover fewer topics well than to cover many topics poorly.

The following pages identify the GAISE recommendations. The author comments included about the GAISE recommendations are designed to clarify the above points.

GAISE Recommendations

GAISE is an acronym for "Guidelines for Assessment and Instruction in Statistics Education." These guidelines are recommendations from a project sponsored by the American Statistical Association (ASA). Here are six GAISE recommendations for the teaching of introductory statistics:

1. **Emphasize statistical literacy and develop statistical thinking;**
2. **Use real data;**
3. **Stress conceptual understanding rather than mere knowledge of procedures;**
4. **Foster active learning in the classroom;**
5. **Use technology for developing conceptual understanding and analyzing data;**
6. **Use assessments to improve and evaluate student learning;**

The author enthusiastically supports these recommendations, and much of the content of this *Insider's Guide* is devoted to implementation of these recommendations. Here are some comments about the six recommendations.

1. **Emphasize statistical literacy and develop statistical thinking.**
The importance of sound sampling techniques should be introduced early and often throughout the introductory statistics course. Part of "literacy" is understanding the meaning of terms such as *simple random sample* and *voluntary response sample*. Statistical thinking is used when a student recognizes that results obtained from a poorly selected sample might be results without any real validity. For example, newspapers, magazines, television shows, and Internet sites often conduct surveys by asking people to respond to some question. However, the responses constitute a voluntary response sample, and students should know that any conclusions based on such a sample do not apply to the larger population of all Americans. This is one simple example of the type of critical thinking that should be fostered throughout the course.

In teaching the introductory statistics course, it is not important to memorize formulas or the detailed mechanics of statistical methods. It is not important to be able to reproduce the formula for the standard deviation s, and it is not so important to be able to do the arithmetic required for manually computing values of standard deviations. Instead, it is important to *understand* what the standard deviation s measures. On a very basic level, it is important for students to know quite well that s is a measure of *variation*. It is *really* important that students develop an ability to *understand* and *interpret* values of the standard deviation s. The empirical rule and Chebyshev's theorem are commonly presented as tools that help students understand and interpret s, but the author recommends skipping those two topics and focusing instead on the *range rule of thumb* presented in the book. It is easy to apply, and students generally understand it quite well, so it becomes a very effective tool that can help students understand and interpret values of standard deviations. This topic will be discussed further when measures of variation are discussed later in this guide. But this topic is excellent for making the point that we should emphasize statistical literacy and develop statistical thinking.

When teaching an introductory calculus course, the author might give a test question that asks students to write the definition of the derivative of the function $f(x)$, and he might ask students to compute the derivative of $f(x) = x^2$ while showing all of the steps involved. Calculus students should know the definition of the derivative and they should be able to apply it. However, the author would never ask statistics students to write the formula for the standard deviation or to calculate the standard deviation of a list of values while showing all work. Instead, the author prefers to ask questions that test *understanding*. Here are examples of good and bad test questions:

Bad test question: Write the formulas for the mean and standard deviation s, then compute the mean and standard deviation of the values 23.7, 11.2, 43.5, 77.2, 49.0, 27.3, and show all work.

Good test question: Listed below are weights (in grams) of newly minted quarters. (a) Find the mean. (b) Find the standard deviation. (c) In the context of the given weights, is a weight of 5.23 g *usual* or *unusual*? Explain your choice. (d) What is an adverse consequence of minting quarters with weights that vary too much?

5.71 5.71 5.59 5.61 5.63

When students find the mean $\bar{x} = 5.650$ g and standard deviation of $s = 0.057$ g, they should be encourage to use some technology, such as a TI-83 Plus or TI-84 Plus calculator. There is little to be gained by requiring that such statistics be calculated manually. A good answer to part (b) of the preceding question is the statement that yes, a weight of 5.23 g would be unusual because it is more than two standard deviations away from the mean. One of several good answers to part (c) would be a statement that if weights of minted quarters vary too much, vending machines will reject too many valid coins. Part (c) is designed to emphasize the point that methods of statistics have real, important, and meaningful applications instead of being abstract concepts that might not have any real applications.

2. **Use real data**

George Cobb is a leader in statistics education. He wrote an article about evaluating introductory statistics textbooks (see "Introductory Textbooks: A Framework for evaluation", *Journal of the American Statistical Association*, Vol. 82, No. 397) and he included this statement:

"Are the Data Sets Real or Fake? Not that many years ago, all it took was this first question to dispatch most books to the morgue. Fortunately, that is changing. It is true that there are still books on the market whose examples have been bled white of vital detail, but it is now easier to shun them. I hope that soon we will have seen the last of the infamous XYZ Corporation and Hospitals A, B, C, ..."

With real data, students see how statistical concepts have meaningful applications. Hopefully, they will encounter data from the discipline that they might be considering as a major.

3. **Stress conceptual understanding rather than mere knowledge of procedures**
A good illustration of this point can be seen in the data from eruptions of the Old Faithful geyser and data from forecast and actual low temperatures:

Duration (sec)	240	120	178	234	235	269	255	220
Interval After (min)	92	65	72	94	83	94	101	87

Actual low (°F)	54	54	55	60	64
Low forecast five days earlier (°F)	56	57	59	56	64

When discussing correlation/regression, we might present the top table and ask if there is a correlation between the duration of an eruption and the time interval after the eruption to the next eruption. When discussing matched data, we might present the second table given above, and we might ask if the differences between the actual and forecast temperatures are from a population with a mean of 0. But instead of focusing too much on the details of the computations involved, we should stress the fundamental difference between the two sets of data summarized in the preceding tables. Students should learn how to ask the best questions. Given the first table above, students should see that the issue is one of a *relationship* between the two variables. Given the second table above, students should see that a key element is the list of *differences* between the actual and forecast temperatures, and a mean difference equal to zero is evidence that the forecast temperatures are accurate. It's not the structure of paired data that determines the method that is most appropriate, it is the *context* of the data.

4. **Foster active learning in the classroom**
Here is an old saying that is so true when considered in the context of teaching an introductory statistics course:

Tell me something, and I will forget.
Show me and I will remember.
Involve me, and I will learn.

If you want your students to have a learning experience that will affect them for their entire lives, *involve* them with active learning. The textbook has Cooperative Group Activities at the end of each chapter. Also, see Chapter 15 of *Elementary Statistics,* 10th edition, for a long list of additional project topics.

Some statistics professors believe that the entire course should be based on activities, and some other statistics professors do not include any activities at all. Somewhere between these extremes is a balance that allows active involvement along with enough time for teaching concepts using traditional methods.

Recommendation: If you do no activities at all, begin with just one or two activities to see how well they work. Then, assuming that all goes well, incorporate more activities in your course in the future.

5. Use technology for developing conceptual understanding and analyzing data

Many statistics professors teach an effective course by allowing students to use any one of a variety of different scientific calculators. The author recommends that a specific technology be used. The Triola statistics books include displays from STATDISK, Minitab, Excel, and a TI-83/84 Plus calculator. There are also supplements for SPSS and SAS.

The author's personal preference is to require that each student have a TI-83 Plus or TI-84 Plus calculator, and that each student also do several software projects using STATDISK. However, choosing a technology to be used for an introductory statistics course is a complex decision that must take several factors into account. Some colleges have adopted a decision to use Excel because so many students use Excel in their work after graduation. Some colleges avoid Excel because its statistics functions are not as good as they should be. Some colleges use Minitab, and the latest release includes features that make it a perfectly good choice. Some statistics professors prefer to require TI-83/84 Plus calculators because they can do so much statistical number crunching and they can be used in class and on tests. Some statistics professors would like to require TI-83/84 Plus calculators, but are reluctant to do so because of their cost. The author had that same concern the first time that he required those calculators, so he announced that any students could sell their calculators at the end of the course. At the end of that semester, *no* students wanted to give up their calculators. Their desire to keep their calculators instead of turning them in for cash was a strong indication about how they perceived the usefulness of those calculators.

STATDISK STATDISK is a free easy-to-use software package designed specifically for the Triola statistics books. The latest version of STATDISK is one that the author is proud to have as a major and important supplement. It has been completely recoded and tested since the last release. Because STATDISK can do almost all of the functions described in the textbook, it can be used as the technology in the introductory statistics course. If another technology, such as Excel or SPSS, is used as the major technology, it would be really helpful to have students use STATDISK as a supplement to the main technology being used.

Technology for New Approaches The technology can do the statistics number crunching, but it should also be used to explore concepts and new approaches. When considering the effects of an outlier, for example, a hypothesis test could be conducted with the outlier included and again with the outlier excluded. Probability can be better studied with simulations. Bootstrap resampling techniques can sometimes be used when traditional methods should not be used. For ideas about how to include technology, see the Technology Projects at the ends of the chapters

6. **Use assessments to improve and evaluate student learning**

Traditional tests and quizzes are one important method of assessment, but there are others. The author favors the use of activities and at least one major project. The author favors a capstone group project conducted near the end of the course. Students can work together in groups of four (more or less), and each group should conduct a project that involves the planning of an experiment or a method for collecting data in an observational study. After collecting original data, the group will make an inference by using the methods learned in the course. A group presentation would involve each member speaking for at least a minute or two. A computer display would also be included, along with a brief written report. Assessment is an important component of such a project. How do you assess the work of individual members that participate in a group project? Here is a one method that the author found to be effective: Survey each group member and ask him or her to assess the work done by the other group members. For example, ask each group member to submit a separate form for each other group member. The form should include the name of the other group member and an assessment of their work, such as "was a major contributor to the project," "did an average amount of work on the project," "did some but little work on the project," or "did not participate in any meaningful way." Students are quite honest about the work of their peers, and they along with their peers are quite satisfied with this process of assessment.

The author favors four or five tests given during the semester, along with a comprehensive final examination. Activities and projects should also be part of the assessment plan.

III. Chapter and Section Comments, Activities, Examples, Objectives, and Recommended Exercises

The following items correspond to chapters and sections in *Elementary Statistics,* 10th edition. Whenever time references are made, these following comments assume that an individual class session is approximately one hour. Each chapter begins with a general comment, then individual sections have comments along with activities, extra examples, minimum outcome objectives, and recommended assignments.

Chapter 1

First Class Session The first class of the introductory statistics course will likely involve introductions, distribution of course outlines and course policies, and a clear description of how grades are determined. This first class meeting should involve a description of course priorities, the technology to be used, and a description of any major projects.

- State that this course does not place highest priorities on mathematical computations. Instead, technology can be used to obtain results, but the emphasis is on *understanding* and *interpreting* those results. (See the preceding discussion under the heading of "Emphasize statistical literacy and develop statistical thinking.")

- Announce the technology to be used in the course. ("All students will be required to have a TI-83 Plus or TI-84 Plus calculator," or "all classes will be in the computer lab where STATDISK will be used," or "all students will be required to use Excel," etc.)

- Identify any major projects that will be required. (*Example:* All students will work in groups of three or four to collect original data and apply some method of inferential statistics to form conclusions. The project will involve an oral class presentation, a brief written report, and printed computer results.)

After introductions, distribution of course materials, and announcements such as those given above, there will not be much time left for teaching statistics content. *Suggestion:* Distribute the following survey. Ask that each student complete it now. Collect the completed surveys. If there is time left, discuss the survey by relating it to concepts in Chapter 1 of the textbook. Here are some observations:

- Responses to item 3 are qualitative or categorical data, whereas responses to item 4 are qualitative.

- The survey results constitute a sample of all students at the college, but it is not a representative sample.

- The sample is a convenience sample (instead of random, systematic, stratified, or cluster).
- Item 4 is poorly done because it requires a calculation that can result in errors, and it would be much better to actually measure people than ask them to enter their heights.

- Items 2 and 8 both involve random digits, but item 8 is more likely to yield digits that appear to be random. When people try to select random digits, they often fail because of a bias toward certain digits.

- Is there a relationship between items 9 and 10? It might not be apparent from the results of this survey, but people who exercise vigorously tend to have lower pulse rates.

- As a follow-up to item 8, ask students to identify the 5th digit of their social security number, then ask them to announce those digits while they are recorded. Analyze the digits. It is common to get a small number of even digits or a small number of odd digits. (The 5th digit is used as a geographic locator.)

- Describe the different levels of measurement (nominal, ordinal, interval, ratio) and point out that eye colors for item 3 are nominal data, but heights from item 4 are at the ratio level of measurement. A good test for the ratio level is to determine whether ratios such as "twice" make sense in the context of the data. A height of 6 ft is twice as tall as a height of 3 ft, so heights are at the ratio level of measurement. Point out that it makes sense to do arithmetic computations with data at the ratio level of measurement, but it does not make sense to do certain computations with data at the nominal level of measurement.

The survey results can also be used for illustrations later in the course. Here are two examples:

- Correlation/regression: Use heights (item 4) and pulse rates (item 9).

- Test for a difference between two means: Use pulse rates of males and pulse rates of females.

Triola Survey

Please complete the survey and submit it now. Do not sign your name.

1. _____Female _____Male

2. Randomly select four digits and enter them here: ___ ___ ___ ___

3. Eye color: _______________

4. Enter your height in inches: _______________

5. What is the total value of all coins now in your possession? __________

6. How many keys are in your possession at this time? __________

7. How many credit cards are in your possession at this time? ___

8. Enter the last four digits of your social security number: __ __ __ __

9. Record your pulse rate by counting the number of heartbeats
for one minute: _______________

10. Do you exercise vigorously (such as running, swimming, cycling, tennis, basketball, etc.) for at least 20 minutes at least twice a week?
_____Yes _____No

11. How many credit hours of courses are you taking this semester?
____

12. Are you currently employed? _____Yes _____No
If yes, how many hours do you work each week? __________

13. During the past 12 months, have you been the driver of a car that was involved in a crash? _____Yes _____No

14. Do you smoke? _____Yes _____No

15. _____Left-handed _____Right-handed _____Ambidextrous

1-2 Types of Data

Recommendation: In the first class session, assign Section 1-2 to be read independently, and assign the Section 1-2 exercises given below. Point out that answers to odd-numbered section exercises are in the back of the textbook. You might announce that only the answers to even-numbered exercises will be collected or somehow checked.

Activity: Require completion of the survey on the preceding page, and discuss the survey items that relate to the content of Section 1-2.

Extra Example: The following are the finishing positions of a sample of drivers in a NASCAR race: 3, 8, 12, 15, 27 (3rd place, 8th place, etc.)

a. What is the level of measurement of these data? (Answer: Ordinal)
b. Are these data discrete or continuous? (Answer: Discrete)
c. Are the data qualitative or quantitative? (Answer: Quantitative, because they are counts of cars)

Minimum Outcome Objectives Upon completion of Section 1-2, students should be able to define *parameter, statistic, quantitative data, qualitative* (or *categorical* or *attribute*) *data.* Students should be able to determine whether basic statistical calculations are appropriate for a particular data set.

Recommended assignment:

- Read Sections 1-2 and 1-3.
- In Section 1-2 do Exercises 1-24.
- In Section 1-3 do Exercises 1-20.

1-3 Critical Thinking

Comment that critical thinking is an important component of the course. Students should always question the method of collecting sample data. Be sure that they very clearly understand the concept of a voluntary response sample and the pitfalls associated with such samples. Review the answers to the exercises from this section.

If Section 1-4 is not included in your syllabus, be sure to explain the concepts of a *random sample* and a *simple random sample.*

Activity Consider assigning a short project of collecting current articles or ads that illustrate the misuses discussed in this section. It is not difficult to find examples of the misuse of statistics, especially with graphic illustrations.

Extra Example: During a broadcast of a show on MTV, the host asks viewers to call in and vote for or against a new song, with the result that 74% of 12,335 viewers favor it. Given that the sample is so large and the percentage is so far above 50%, is it valid to conclude that the majority of Americans favor the song? Why or why not? (Answer: No, the respondents are a voluntary response sample, and they do not necessarily reflect the views of all Americans.)

Minimum Outcome Objectives Upon completion of Section 1-3, students should be able to define *voluntary response sample* and determine that statistical conclusions based on data from such a sample are generally not valid. Students should better develop an ability to assess the validity of graphs and other statistical results.

Recommended Assignment: Exercises 1-20 (if they have not yet been assigned)

1-4 Design of Experiments

Students should understand the definitions of *random sample* and *simple random sample*, and appreciate the importance of sound sampling methods.

Activity: Use numbers on slips of paper to randomly select one row of students, then ask if each student in the class has the same chance of being selected (random sample), and whether each sample of the same size has the same chance of being selected (simple random sample). By selecting a row, the sample is a random sample, but not a simple random sample (because it would not be possible to select a sample of the same size with students in different rows).

Extra Example: If you conduct a nationwide survey by randomly selecting 20 people in each state, is the result a simple random sample? Why or why not? (Answer: No. Not all samples of 1000 people have the same chance of being selected. For example, a sample of 1000 from California has no chance of being selected.)

Minimum Outcome Objectives Upon completion of Section 1-4, students should be able to define *random sample* and *simple random sample*, and determine whether a particular sample is a random sample and/or a simple random sample. Students should be able to describe the importance of sound sampling methods and the importance of good design of experiments.

Recommended Assignment: Exercises 1-20 and 25-30.

Chapter 2

Recommendation: Cover Sections 2-2 (Frequency Distributions) and 2-3 (Histograms) together in one class. If you are confident that you have planned the course syllabus so that time allows it, also include Section 2-4 (Statistical Graphics). If Section 2-4 is not included, strongly stress a key point of that section: There are many different types of graphs being used for depicting data, and some graphs are much more effective than others.

2-2 Frequency Distributions
2-3 Histograms

Cover Sections 2-2 (Frequency Distributions) and 2-3 (Histograms) together in one class. Describe the characteristics of data that are often important: center, variation, distribution, outliers, change over time (CVDOT). Refer to Table 2-2 in the textbook and explain how that table summarizes the list of ages. Describe the class width, class limits, class boundaries, and class midpoint values.

Do not use too much valuable class time describing the details of manually constructing a frequency distribution and histogram. Instead, demonstrate them with the following class activity.

Activity: Ask that each student estimate the length of the classroom. (If you want to use less time, use the pulse rates from the survey that was given in the first class.) Collect the anonymous estimates and show how to construct a frequency distribution. Compare the result to the actual length. Do the estimates tend to center about the actual length, or do students tend to underestimate or overestimate the length? After constructing a frequency distribution, identify the class limits, class midpoint, class boundaries, and class width. Then construct the corresponding histogram and show how the graph is much easier to understand than the table of numbers.

Extra Example: If you were to construct a histogram representing 1000 rolls of a fair die, then construct another histogram representing the heights of 1000 randomly selected women, what would those histograms look like, and how would they be different? (Answer: The histogram for the die would be essentially flat, whereas the histogram of the heights would be roughly bell-shaped.)

Minimum Outcome Objectives Upon completion of Sections 2-2 and 2-3, students should be able to define *frequency distribution* and determine whether a potential frequency distribution actually satisfies the necessary requirements. They should also develop the ability to construct a histogram and make a conclusion about the nature of a distribution by examining a histogram.

Recommended assignment: Section 2-2 Exercises 1-18, 20, 22;
Section 2-3 Exercises 1-12.

2-4 Statistical Graphics

Recommendation: Don't require that students learn how to construct all of the graphs included in this section. Instead, discuss stemplots and scatterplots and assign some exercises so that students can experience a variety of graphs, and focus on the art of selecting the graph that does the best job of revealing the true nature of the data set being considered. In many cases, the true nature of the data can be revealed by an original graph different from any of those included in this section.

If Section 2-4 is not included in the syllabus, scatterplots will be covered later in Chapter 10, but it would be helpful to briefly describe stemplots.

Activity: (See the first Cooperative Group Activity.) Refer to Figure 2-10 for the graph that Florence Nightingale constructed roughly 150 years ago. That graph illustrates the numbers of soldiers dying from combat wounds, preventable diseases, and other causes. Figure 2-10 is not very easy to understand. Create a new graph that depicts the same data, but create the new graph in a way that greatly simplifies understanding.

Extra Example: The scatterplot shown below results from 10 subjects each taking two different versions of the same test that is designed to measure creativity. What does the graph suggest about the two tests? (Answer: There does not appear to be a relationship between scores from the two versions of the same test. If the test is a valid measure of anything, two different versions should result in scores that are approximately the same, but the scatterplot suggests that the two versions are totally unrelated.)

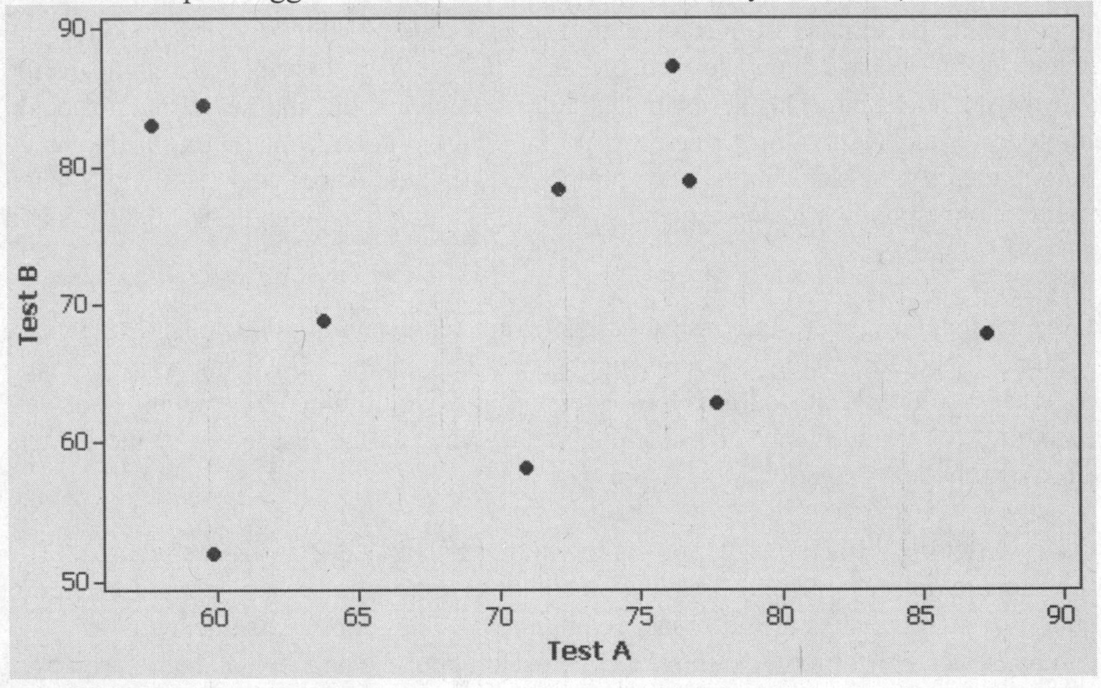

Minimum Outcome Objectives Upon completion of Section 2-4, students should have developed the ability to construct a dotplot, stemplot, and scatterplot. Students should have concluded that there are many different and varied statistical graphs that are effective in allowing us to identify important characteristics of data.

Recommended Assignment: Exercises 1-6, 9, 10, 16, 17, 20-24

Chapter 3

Recommendation: Cover all sections in Chapter 3. Sections 3-2 and 3-3 are each partitioned into two parts: (1) Basic Concepts; (2) Beyond the Basics. If time is an issue, skip the "Beyond the Basics" subsections in Sections 3-2 and 3-3.

3-2 Measures of Center

Recommended approach: Rather than requiring memorization of formulas and requiring that students master the mechanics of manual calculations, allow the use of a computer or calculator for obtaining results, and really stress the *interpretation* of results. But don't totally dismiss manual calculations which have some merit in some cases. On a test, consider allowing students to use a computer or calculator, then ask questions designed to display an *understanding* of the concepts.

Section 3-2 is partitioned into two parts: Part 1 (Basic Concepts of Measures of Center) and Part 2 (Beyond the Basics of Measures of Center). Part 1 introduces the basic definitions of mean, median, mode, and midrange. Part 2 includes frequency distributions, weighted mean, and skewness. *Recommendation*: If you have a typical three credit introductory statistics course that is covered in one semester, cover only Part 1.

Discuss the mean, median, mode, and midrange, and illustrate them with a specific data set. Consider an activity that will generate the data to be used for an illustration. For example, have students draw a line that they estimate to be 4 cm in length. Then use rulers to determine the actual lengths.

Point out that an outlier can have a dramatic effect on the mean, but it does not affect the median so strongly. Also describe the rule for rounding results.

Activity: Collect sample data from the class, then find the mean, median, mode, and midrange. For example, see the first Cooperative Group Activity. As another example, use the pulse rates of males and females. After finding the measures of center for both samples, informally compare them and note that more formal comparisons can be made by using topics from later chapters.

Minimum Outcome Objectives Upon completion of Section 3-2, students should have developed the ability to measure the center of data by finding the mean, median, and mode. They should be able to determine whether an outlier has a substantial effect on the mean, median, and mode.

Extra Example: Here are the volumes (in ounces) of randomly selected cans of Coke: 12.3, 12.1, 12.2, 12.3, 12.2. Find the mean, median, mode, and midrange. (Answer: 12.22, 12.20, 12.2, 12.15.)

Recommended Assignment: 1-12, 16, 17

3-3 Measures of Variation

Variation is an *extremely* important topic in statistics, and this is one of the most important sections in the book, so consider devoting *two* class sessions to this section.

Suggestion: Begin by describing the single line system and the multi-line system used in banks, then ask the class to compare the customer waiting times given below. How do the means differ? (It is the same for both.) Why did so many banks make the change to the single line system? What *does* change? (There is less variation with a single line, and this makes customers happier and less frustrated.) This situation is an ideal introduction to Section 3-3. In class, refer to the following exercise from Section 3-2, and ask half the class to find the mean, median, mode, and midrange for the single-line system while the other half of the class finds the mean, median, mode, and midrange for the multi-line system. Compare the results to see that both systems have the same measures of center. Then ask the class to simply examine and compare the two data sets. What is fundamentally different about the two data sets? (The single line system has times that *vary* much less than the times for the other system.) Because this characteristic of variation is so important, we need to develop a measure for it.

Customer Waiting Times Waiting times (in minutes) of customers at the Jefferson Valley Bank (where all customers enter a single waiting line) and the Bank of Providence (where customers wait in individual lines at three different teller windows) are listed below. Determine whether there is a difference between the two data sets that is not apparent from a comparison of the measures of center. If so, what is it?

Jefferson Valley (single line):	6.5	6.6	6.7	6.8	7.1	7.3	7.4	7.7	7.7	7.7
Providence (multiple lines):	4.2	5.4	5.8	6.2	6.7	7.7	7.7	8.5	9.3	10.0

Now use the values for the single line and develop the formula for the standard deviation as follows.

1. The mean is 7.15. Find the deviation of each value from the mean.
2. Show that the sum of the deviations from Step 1 is 0. Ask if it will always be 0 (the answer is yes).
3. We want to avoid the canceling out of the positive and negative deviations. How do we do that? (Take absolute values or square them.) We will square the deviations.
4. Now we want a single value, so we need a mean of those squared deviations, but we find the mean by dividing by $n - 1$ instead of n.
5. Now track the units. If the original times are in minutes, the deviations are in minutes, the squared deviations are in min^2, and the mean is in min^2.
6. Because we can't really understand min^2 very well, we take the square root to get back to the original units.

After showing how this procedure results in the standard deviation, stress that students need not become adept at the computations required for this formula. Instead, they should learn how to obtain values of standard deviations using calculators or programs, and the real focus should be on *understanding* the standard deviation.

Understanding standard deviation: It is recommended that you use the range rule of thumb. You can skip Chebyshev's theorem and the empirical rule. For the range rule of thumb, randomly select a student and ask for an estimate of the mean height of a male at the college. They usually answer this quite well. Now randomly select another student and ask for an estimate of the standard deviation of heights of males at the college. Give the student just a few seconds before stating that it is perfectly natural to have no idea of the answer. That is the nature of the standard deviation. However, ask the same student for estimates of the minimum and maximum heights. Then use $s \approx \text{range}/4$ to show how easy it is to get an estimate.

Now show how to interpret a known value of a standard deviation. State that typical IQ tests have a mean of 100 and a standard deviation of 15. Using the range rule of thumb, we get these results:

minimum *usual* score $= \bar{x} - 2s = 100 - 2(15) = 70$
maximum *usual* score $= \bar{x} + 2s = 100 + 2(15) = 130$

so that *usual* IQ scores are those between 70 and 130. An IQ of 140 is therefore unusual.

Recommendation: This section is partitioned into two parts: Part 1 (Basic Concepts of Variation) and Part 2 (Beyond the Basics of Variation). If pressed for time, omit Chebyshev's Theorem (because its results are too imprecise), omit the Empirical Rule (because it will be covered in Chapter 6), and omit the coefficient of variation. Strongly emphasize the interpretation and understanding of standard deviation using the Range Rule of Thumb. This is a great way to begin the thought process that will be used later for methods of inferential statistics.

Extra Example: A statistics professor finds that the times (in seconds) required to complete a quiz have a mean of 180 sec and a standard deviation of 30 sec. Is a time of 90 sec unusual? Why or why not? (Answer: Yes, because 90 sec is more than 2 standard deviations below the mean.)

Minimum Outcome Objectives Upon completion of Section 3-3, students should have developed the ability to measure variation in a set of sample data by finding values of the range, variance, and standard deviation. They should have developed the ability to interpret values of the standard deviation by applying the *range rule of thumb* to determine whether a particular value is *unusual*. They should also be able to interpret a value of a standard deviation by determining the minimum usual value and maximum usual value.

Recommended Assignment: Exercises 1-12, 16, 17, 29-32

3-4 Measures of Relative Standing

Students can generally read and understand z scores on their own, so discuss them briefly, but stress the interpretation of z scores using the following criteria:

Ordinary values: $-2 \leq z$ **score** ≤ 2

Unusual values: **z score** < -2 *or* **z–score** > 2

These criteria emphasize the point that it is unusual for a value to be below the mean by more than 2 standard deviations or above the mean by more than 2 standard deviations. This is an excellent preparation for hypothesis testing introduced later. With hypothesis tests using a normal distribution, common critical values are $z = \pm 1.96$, which is roughly 2, so we again use the same basic criterion for identifying *unusual* results.

When discussing quartiles and percentiles, it would be helpful to demonstrate use of the flowchart with two examples, one that results in an integer value of L and one that does not. Refer to the two examples in the textbook that illustrate the use of Figure 3-6; the first example does not result in an integer value of L, but the second example does result in an integer value of L.

Extra Example: Over the past 30 years, heights of basketball players at Newport University have a mean of 74.5 in. and a standard deviation of 2.5 in. The latest recruit has a height of 79.0 in.

a. Find the *z* score. (Answer: 1.80)
b. Is the height of 79.0 in. unusual among the heights of players over the past 30 years? Why or why not? (Answer: No, because it is within 2 standard deviations of the mean.)

Minimum Outcome Objectives Upon completion of Section 3-4, students should have developed the ability to compute a *z* score and use the result to determine whether a given value *x* is *unusual*. They should be able to define *percentiles* and *quartiles*.

Recommended Assignment: 1-4 and the even-numbered exercises from 6 through 26

3-5 Exploratory Data Analysis (EDA)

Be sure to discuss outliers if they have not been discussed much yet. Demonstrate the effect of an outlier by computing the mean and standard deviation of the sample values 1, 1, 2, 3, 8, 165 with and without the outlier of 165 included. Comment that outliers are among the important characteristics of data (CVDOT: center, variation, distribution, outliers, changes over time) and they are important because they can have a dramatic effect on results. If an outlier is found to be a known error, delete it. But if an outlier is believed to be a correct value, do analyses with and without the outlier included so that its effect can be seen.

Also describe the 5-number summary and boxplots, but really emphasize how these tools are used to understand data through descriptions, explorations, and comparisons.

Recommendation: Time is usually an issue, so briefly mention modified boxplots, but do not require that students develop the ability to create modified boxplots on their own.

Extra Example: Here are measured reaction times (in seconds) in a test of driving skills: 2.4, 2,5, 2.8, 2.0, 2.4, 2.9, 3.2, 3.5, 2.7, 2.7, 2.8, 2.6. Find the five-number-summary. (Answer: 2.0, 2.45, 2.7, 2.85, 3.5)

Minimum Outcome Objectives Upon completion of Section 3-5, students should have developed the abilities to describe and identify *outliers*, to construct a boxplot from a given set of sample data, and describe the nature of the distribution by examining the boxplot.

Recommended Assignment: Exercises 1–8. Be sure to comment that if students generate boxplots using calculators or computers, the quartile values may differ somewhat from those given as answers in this text.

Chapter 4

Probability is important as a foundation for very basic methods of statistics. For example, hypothesis tests often include a result of a "*P*-value," which is actually a probability value. It is important to understand that probability values are numbers between 0 and 1, and small probabilities, such as 0.001, correspond to events that are very unlikely, whereas high probabilities, such as 0.999, correspond to events that are very likely.

Some professors choose to include extensive coverage of probability theory by covering all of Chapter 4, while other professors choose to minimize the coverage of probability by including only section 4-2.

Recommendations: If time is an issue or if the students have minimal mathematics backgrounds, include only Section 4-2. If time is not too much of an issue, include Section 4-2 (Fundamentals), 4-3 (Addition Rule), and Section 4-4 (Multiplication Rule: Basics). If time is not an issue and the students have strong mathematics backgrounds, include additional sections of Chapter 4.

Recommendation: If Section 4-6 is not included, consider doing a class activity that demonstrates the use of simulations. For example, find the probability of getting at least 3 consecutive girls when 5 babies are born, but simulate births by having each student flip a coin 5 times.

4-2 Fundamentals

Recommendation: Instead of discussing probability as a separate and independent topic, relate it to statistical methods by including the rare event rule for inferential statistics.

Rare Event Rule for Inferential Statistics

> **If, under a given assumption, the probability of a particular observed event is extremely small, we conclude that the assumption is probably not correct.**

Section 4-2 covers basic definitions and simple concepts of probability. Emphasize the importance of *understanding* the available data, because some students tend to develop this rule for finding probabilities: Find two numbers, then divide the smaller number by the larger one. For class examples, include at least one example where that rule doesn't work. For example, if a quality control test shows that there are 5 defective printers and there are 15 that are good, the probability of randomly selecting one that is defective is 5/20, not 5/15.

Also, stress that the usual goal is not to simply find a probability value, but to use it for making some decision. Many exercises ask questions requiring the *interpretation* of probability values.

Recommendation: If pressed for time, omit the subsection of *odds*.

Activity: Give each student a thumb tack and ask them to find the probability that the tack lands with the point up. Is the answer 0.5, because the tack either lands with the point up or does not? Why or why not?

Extra Example: A medical center has 18 female physicians and 2 male physicians.

a. If a patient randomly selects one of the physicians, what is the probability of getting a male? (Answer: 1/10 or 0.1)

b. Is it unusual for a patient to get a male when a physician is randomly selected? Why or why not? (Answer: No, because the probability of 0.1 is not small, such as 0.05 or less.)

Minimum Outcome Objectives Upon completion of Section 4-2, students should identify probability values as values between 0 and 1. They should determine whether an event is unusual by assessing the probability value, and they should have developed the ability to calculate probabilities of events. They should be able to describe the classical definition of probability by including the statement that it requires equally likely outcomes. They should be able to define the *complement* of an event and calculate the probability of that complement.

Recommended Assignment: 1-14, 18-24. (*Notes:* Exercises 17-24 emphasize the use of probability values for determining whether events are "unusual." Exercises 29-32 involve odds.)

4-3 Addition Rule

Point out that the key point of this section is that *P*(*A* or *B*) suggests the addition rule; associate "or" with adding. Avoid double counting of events that are not mutually exclusive. Emphasize use of the intuitive rule instead of the formal rule, because the intuitive rule is based on understanding of circumstances instead of blind application of a formula. Point out that a table such as Table 4-1 is called a *two-way* table or *contingency* table, and such tables are very important in statistics because they arise frequently from analysis of survey results. Such tables are the focus of Section 11-3.

Extra Example: Considerable controversy arose when New York City introduced a program of keeping the cars belonging to people charged with drunk driving. The Associated Press conducted a poll, and the table below is based on the results. If one of the respondents is randomly selected, find the probability of getting a man or someone who answered yes. (Answer: 1296/1552 = 0.835)

	Should Car Be Seized?	
	Yes	No
Men	391	425
Women	480	256

Minimum Outcome Objectives Upon completion of Section 4-3, students should have developed the ability to calculate the probability that in a single trial, some event *A* occurs or some event *B* occurs or they both occur. Students should be able to apply the addition rule by correctly adjusting for events that are not disjoint.

Recommended Assignment: Exercises 1- 12, 21, 22

4-4 Multiplication Rule: Basics

The basic multiplication rule is very important because it has implications affecting many real applications. Redundancy, for example, is the practice of using duplicate or backup systems to greatly increase reliability. The typical single engine aircraft uses redundancy with two separate and independent electrical systems. The improved reliability can be measured by applying the basic multiplication rule. Illustrate this with specific numbers. For example, suppose the probability of one electrical system failing is 0.1. Then there is a 0.9 probability of a safe flight. But with two electrical systems, the probability of them both failing is $0.1 \times 0.1 = 0.01$, so there is now a 0.99 probability of a safe flight.

Key points of this section: *P*(*A* and *B*) suggests multiplication; adjust probabilities for *dependent* events.

Notation: In this section, *P*(*A* and *B*) denotes that event *A* occurs in one trial and event *B* occurs in another trial; in Section 4-3 we used *P*(*A* and *B*) to denote that events *A* and *B* both occur in the same trial.

Emphasize the intuitive rule that doesn't depend on blind application of a formula. Many instructors have much greater success with the intuitive rule than the formal rule.

Extra Example: A homeowner finds that there is a 0.1 probability that a flashlight does not work when turned on. If she has three flashlights, find the probability that none of them work when there is a power failure. (Answer: $0.1^3 = 0.001$)

Activity: Simulate the principle of redundancy by using coin tosses to simulate the starting of a car. Assume that a student has access to a fleet of cars, but each of the cars is old and has a 50% chance of starting. If the student needs a car to get to class, what is the probability of getting there if the "fleet" has only one such car? Two cars? Three cars?

Minimum Outcome Objectives Upon completion of Section 4-4, students should have developed the ability to calculate the probability of an event A occurring in a first trial and an event B occurring in a second trial. They should be able to apply the multiplication rule by adjusting for events that are not independent. They should be able to distinguish between independent events and dependent events.

Recommended Assignment: Exercises 1-14, 17-20

4-5 Multiplication Rule: Complements and Conditional Probability

This section is partitioned into two separate subsections:

Complements: The Probability of "At Least One"
Conditional Probability

You could include either or both of these subsections.

In the first subsection, students often have some difficulty with the key concept. Begin by clearly explaining the meaning of "at least one." Then discuss the complement of "at least one." Then emphasize this key point: To find *P*(at least one something), it's usually better to first find the probability of the complement, then subtract from 1.

To find the probability of *at least one* of something, calculate the probability of *none*, then subtract that result from 1. That is,

$$P(\text{at least one}) = 1 - P(\text{none}).$$

In the second subsection of *conditional probability,* emphasize careful reading and understanding of the available information and the probability being sought. Emphasize the intuitive approach described in this subsection.

Extra Example: A homeowner finds that there is a 0.1 probability that a flashlight does *not* work when turned on.

a. If she has three flashlights, find the probability that at least one of them works when there is a power failure. (Answer: 0.999)
b. Find the probability that the second flashlight works given that the first flashlight works. (Answer: 0.9)

Minimum Outcome Objectives Upon completion of Section 4-5, students should have developed the ability to compute the probability of "at least one" occurrence of an event A. They should also be able to apply the multiplication rule by computing the probability of some event, given that some other event has already occurred.

Recommended Assignment: Exercises 1-18

4-6 Probabilities through Simulations

Suggestion: Assign this section as reading to be done by the student, but do the following activity in class. This exercise is one that students easily understand, and its solution is not so obvious, but the solution becomes obvious through simulations.

Activity: Have students pair off and address Exercise 15 (the Monty Hall problem).

Extra Example: Bring an old telephone book to class, and give each student a page from it. Ask them to simulate spins of a roulette wheel by randomly selecting one of the numbers 0, 1, 2, 3, …, 37. Note that a roulette wheel does not have a 37, so let 37 represent the outcome of 00. (Roulette wheels have slots for 0 and 00 and the numbers 1, 2, 3, …, 36.) Have students "play" roulette by betting on the number 7 each time. Collect results from several simulated spins from each student, and use the combined results to estimate the probability of getting a 7. (Answer: The answers will vary, but they should be around 1/38 or 0.0263.)

Minimum Outcome Objectives Upon completion of Section 4-6, students should have developed the ability to construct a simulation of a procedure, so that they can better understand the behavior of the procedure.

Recommended Assignment: Exercises 1-4, 9, 10

4-7 Counting

Some professors feel strongly that this section should be included, but it can be easily omitted.

Recommendation: Unless you have an abundance of time, such as the time available in a two-semester course, omit this section, but consider demonstrating the combinations rule for finding the probability of winning a lottery, as in Exercise 13.

Activity: Identify the lottery rules of your state, and shown the probability of winning the grand prize. Then relate that probability to something tangible and concrete, such as the probability of selecting one particular dime in a pile of dimes. How high would the pile be?

Extra Example: Singing legend Frank Sinatra recorded 381 songs. From a list of his top-10 songs, you must select 3 that will be sung in a medley as a tribute at the next MTV Music Awards ceremony. The order of the songs is important so that they fit together well. If you select 3 of Sinatra's top-10 songs, how many different sequences are possible? (Answer: 720 permutations)

Minimum Outcome Objectives Upon completion of Section 4-7, students should have developed the ability to apply the fundamental counting rule, factorial rule, permutations rule, and combinations rule. They should be able to distinguish between circumstances requiring the permutations rule and those requiring the combinations rule.

Recommended Assignment: Exercises 1-16, 27-30

4-8 Bayes' Theorem

The presentation of Bayes' Theorem is not included in the textbook itself, but it is on the CD-ROM included with new copies of the textbook. Most textbooks describe application of Bayes' Theorem through calculations with formulas, but this discussion presents an alternative method that is much easier to understand and apply.

Chapter 5

Recommendation: Cover Sections 5-2, 5-3, and 5-4, but omit Section 5-5 (Poisson Distribution) unless time is not an issue.

Section 5-4 and quick and relatively easy, so it could be combined with Section 5-3 or it could be covered in half of one class.

5-2 Random Variables

Suggestion: List two samples of data, each with about 20 values. Create one sample consisting of 20 single digits with approximately equal frequencies of 0, 1, 2, . . . , 9 and select the other sample to be 20 digits that are mostly 0s and 5s with a few other digits thrown in. Inform the class that both samples are the *last* digits of recorded weights of people, but one of the samples came from *measured* weights whereas the other sample resulted from *asking* people what they weighed. Ask the class to distinguish between the reported weights and the measured weights. Emphasize that they can make a conclusion about the nature of the data by simply examining the distribution. Also ask them to construct an "ideal" distribution that would result from millions of people that were actually weighed; ask them to estimate the mean and standard deviation for this distribution. (The mean should be 4.5 and the standard deviation could be estimated using the range rule of thumb; the true mean is 4.5 and the true standard deviation is around 3.)

When discussing the mean and standard deviation for a probability distribution, stress that obtaining numerical answers is not the ultimate goal. We want to *interpret* results so that they can be applied in a meaningful way. This process of determining whether events are "unusual" is extremely important in the subject of statistics, and it forms the foundation for the important methods of hypothesis testing introduced in Chapter 8. Discuss the following criteria.

Using Probabilities to Determine When Results Are Unusual

- **Unusually high number of successes:** x successes among n trials is an *unusually high* number of successes if $P(x \text{ or more}) \leq 0.05^*$.
- **Unusually low number of successes:** x successes among n trials is an *unusually low* number of successes if $P(x \text{ or fewer}) \leq 0.05^*$.

*The value of 0.05 is commonly used, but is not absolutely rigid. Other values, such as 0.01, could be used to distinguish between events that can easily occur by chance and events that are very unlikely to occur by chance.

Extra Example: The random variable x is a count of the number of girls that occur when two babies are born. Construct a table representing the probability distribution, then find its mean and standard deviation. (Answer: The values of 0, 1, 2 have probabilities of 0.25, 0.50, and 0.25; the mean is 1.0 and the standard deviation is 1.0.)

Minimum Outcome Objectives Upon completion of Section 5-2, students should be able to define *random variable* and *probability distribution.* They should be able to determine when a potential probability distribution actually satisfies the necessary requirements. Given a particular probability distribution, students should be able to compute the mean and standard deviation, then use those results to determine whether results are *unusual*.

Recommended Assignment: Exercises 1-14, 17-19.

5-3 Binomial Probability Distributions

When introducing the notation used in the binomial probability formula, strongly emphasize that x counts *successes* and p is the probability of *success*, so x and p must both refer to the same outcome. A common error is to have x count one category of outcome while p is the probability of the other category of outcome. Students also have some difficulty with the probability p; strongly emphasize that p is the probability of getting a success on just *one* trial.

Although the emphasis in the course should not be on calculations with formulas, it is helpful to have students do a few calculations that require use of the formula. Here's a good strategy for using Formula 5-5: Get a single number for $n!/[(n-x)!x!]$, get a single number for p^x and a single number for q^{n-x}; then multiply the three factors together. Also, point out the common calculator error of evaluating a/bc by entering a ÷ b × c; the correct entry is obtained by entering either a ÷ b ÷ c or a ÷ (b × c).

In class, make up a few problems that can be solved with the table in the margin of the book, and be sure that students learn how to use it correctly. Examples: Find the probability that among 12 jurors, the number of Mexican-Americans is (a) exactly 10; (b) more than 10; (c) at least 10; (d) fewer than 10.

If you are not using a specific technology such as STATDISK, Minitab, Excel, or a TI-83/84 Plus calculator, comment that it is helpful to be able to interpret displayed results from such technologies. Consider providing such displays on tests, then asking questions about the results.

Activity: Point out to students that they have an opportunity of winning $1,000,000. Do the first Cooperative Group Activity.

Extra Example: Find the probability of getting exactly 3 girls when 5 babies are born. Is that event unusual? Why or why not? (Answer: 0.312; no, because the probability is not small, such as 0.05 or less.)

Minimum Outcome Objectives Upon completion of Section 5-3, students should be able to describe a binomial probability distribution and find probability values for a binomial distribution.

Recommended Assignment: Exercises 1-8, 13-18, 21, 22, 29, 30. (These exercises require calculations with the binomial probability formula: Exercises 21-24, 31-36.)

5-4 Mean, Variance, and Standard Deviation for the Binomial Distribution

The calculations and concepts of this section are generally quite easy. If pressed for time, this section could be assigned as reading without taking class time for discussion.

Recommendation: The *interpretation* of standard deviations should be stressed and reviewed, as in part b of the second example in Section 5-4. The ultimate goal is not to simply obtain a numerical result, but to interpret that result in a practical and meaningful way. Also, determining whether a result is "unusual" is excellent preparation for the method of hypothesis testing introduced in Chapter 8.

Extra Example: In a test of a gender-selection technique, 150 couples each have one baby, and the results consist of 100 girls and 50 boys.

a. Find the mean and standard deviation for the numbers of girls that would occur in groups of 150 births. (Answer: 75, 6.1)

b. Is the result of 100 girls unusual? Why or why not? (Answer: Yes, because 100 is more than 2 standard deviations away from the mean of 75.)

Minimum Outcome Objectives Upon completion of Section 5-4, students should have developed the ability to compute the mean and standard deviation for a binomial distribution, then use those results to determine whether results are *unusual*.

Recommended Assignment: Exercises 1-10, 19, 20.

5-5 The Poisson Distribution

Recommendation: This section is not necessary for subsequent chapters and may be omitted. Include this section only if you are confident that you will have sufficient time for more important topics covered later in your course.

Extra Example: A barber finds that on Fridays between 4:00 PM and 5:00 PM, the mean number of arrivals is 6.0. If the arrivals follow a Poisson distribution, find the probability of getting exactly 3 arrivals during that time. Is it unusual to get exactly 3 arrivals? (Answer: 0.0892; no, because the probability is not small, such as 0.05 or less.)

Minimum Outcome Objectives After completing Section 5-5, students should be able to describe a Poisson probability distribution and find probability values for a Poisson distribution.

Recommended Assignment: Exercises 1-11, 14

Chapter 6

Sections 6-2 through 6-5 are *extremely* important. Before beginning the chapter, stress that much of the content of this chapter will be used often throughout the remainder of the course, so it very important to learn that content well as soon as possible.

Recommendation: Cover Sections 6-2 through 6-5. Comment that Section 6-7 includes methods for determining whether sample data appear to come from a population having a normal distribution. Students have already worked with histograms which can be used for that purpose. If Section 6-7 is omitted, it might be worthwhile commenting on normal quantile plots and describing how they can be used to assess normality, without getting into the details of how they are constructed. Section 6-6 (Normal as Approximation to Binomial) can be omitted because technology now allows us to find exact probabilities for most binomial experiments, so the normal approximation is becoming obsolete.

Be sure to inform your students of the materials that will be available to them on tests. *Recommendation:* Allow students to use the detachable Formula/Table card found in the book, which includes a copy of Table A-2. You might formally state that students should not write notes on that Formula/Table card.

6-2 The Standard Normal Distribution

Stress that Section 6-2 is *extremely* important because it introduces concepts and procedures that will be used often throughout the remainder of the course.

Constantly stress the difference between *areas* under the curve and z scores that are *distances* representing the number of standard deviations that a value is away from the mean. Note that the numbers in the body of Table A-2 are areas and the numbers in the extreme left column (and across the top row) are z scores that are actually distances. If a z score is to the *left* of the centerline, it must be negative. It's always a good idea to check answers to be sure that they are reasonable.

Recommendation: Require or strongly encourage the drawing of a graph for each problem solved. Point out that the graph provides a visual understanding that can be really helpful when solving the problems of this important chapter.

Because the content of this section is so important for subsequent sections and chapters, consider giving a quick quiz on the content of this section. Announce such quizzes in advance. Surprise quizzes only add to anxiety, which is best kept at a minimum.

Extra Example: Given that the distribution of the random variable z is a standard normal distribution, find the probability of randomly selecting a z value between -0.97 and 2.83. (Answer: 0.8317 or 0.8316 if using technology)

Minimum Outcome Objectives After completing Section 6-2, students should have developed the ability to describe a standard normal distribution. They should be able to find the probability of some range of values in a standard normal distribution. They should be able to find z scores corresponding to regions under the curve representing a standard normal distribution.

Recommended Assignment: Exercises 1-28, 37–40. This is actually a reasonable assignment and is not as long as it might seem. Remember, answers to odd-numbered exercises are found in Appendix E.

6-3 Applications of Normal Distributions

State that this section involves *nonstandard* normal distributions, which do not have $\mu = 0$ and $\sigma = 1$. After using the simple transformation of $z = (x - \mu)/\sigma$, we can use the same basic procedures presented in Section 6-2. If students have not yet mastered the procedures from Section 6-2, they should definitely go back and master them before continuing.

Recommendation: Require that students draw a graph for each problem.

Extra Example: Assume that body temperatures of healthy adults are normally distributed with a mean of 98.20°F and a standard deviation of 0.62°F.

a. Find the probability of randomly selecting someone with a body temperature above 99.90°F. Is such a temperature unusual? (Answer: 0.0031; yes, because its probability is small --- below 0.05.)

b. Find P_{20}. (Answer: 97.68°F)

Minimum Outcome Objectives After completing Section 6-3, students should have developed the ability to describe a normal distribution. They should be able to find the probability of some range of values in a normal distribution. They should be able to find x scores corresponding to regions under the curve representing a normal distribution.

Recommended Assignment: Exercises 1–16, 20-22

6-4 Sampling Distributions and Estimators

Recommendation: Assign this section as reading to be done before discussing important points in class.

This section is designed to introduce the general concept of a sampling distribution of a statistic, and to demonstrate that some statistics (mean, variance, proportion) tend to target a population parameter while others do not.

This section includes a paragraph with a heading of "Why sample with replacement?" It is important to recognize why sampling with replacement is so important, given that sampling without replacement is used most often. Comment on the content of this paragraph.

After completing this section, students should know that a sampling distribution of a statistic (such as a sample proportion or sample mean) is the distribution of all values of the statistic when all possible samples of the same size n are taken from the same population. The sampling distribution of a statistic is typically represented as a probability distribution in the format of a table, probability histogram, or formula. They should know that the mean, variance, and proportion tend to target a population parameter while some other statistics do not.

Minimum Outcome Objectives After completing Section 6-4, students should have developed the ability to describe a *sampling distribution of a statistic,* and determine whether a statistic serves as a good estimator of the corresponding population parameter.

Recommended Assignment: Exercises 1-8, 11, 14

6-5 The Central Limit Theorem

Activity: Try motivating the important concepts of this section: Ask each student to announce the last four digits of his or her social security number. As they respond, construct a dotplot on the blackboard and show that it depicts a distribution that is approximately uniform. Then ask each student to compute the mean of the same four digits, and proceed to show that the sample means tend to have a bell-shaped distribution. Also, the mean of the sample means should be the same as the mean of the original list of digits. Finally, question the class and try to draw out the fact that the amount of *variation* among the sample means is less than the amount of variation present in the original list of digits. (The sample means will be closer together than the original list of digits.)

In class, be sure to do an example similar in nature to the second example in this section. Do part (a) with *one* individual selected, and do part (b) with a *group* selected. Point out that with one individual, we use $z = (x - \mu)/\sigma$, but with a group of values we replace σ with $\sigma/\sqrt{n}$.

Finite Population Correction Factor Because of time limitations, many instructors choose to omit coverage of the finite population correction factor. If the finite population correction factor is omitted, do not assign Exercises 22 and 23 (located in the group of exercises labeled "Beyond the Basics").

Extra Example: Assume that body temperatures of healthy adults are normally distributed with a mean of 98.20°F and a standard deviation of 0.62°F.

a. If one healthy adult is randomly selected, find the probability that his or her temperature is greater than 99.00°F. (Answer: 0.0985)

b. If 9 healthy adults are randomly selected, find the probability that their mean body temperature is greater than 99.00°F. (Answer: 0.0001)

Minimum Outcome Objectives After completing Section 6-5, students should be able to describe the central limit theorem. They should be able to apply the central limit theorem by finding the probability that for some collection of sample values, the sample mean falls within some specified range of values. Students should also be able to identify conditions for which it is appropriate to use a normal distribution for the distribution of sample means.

Recommended Assignment: Exercises 1-10, 17-20. (Exercises 22 and 23 require the finite population correction factor.)

6-6 Normal as Approximation to Binomial

Using software or a TI-83/84 Plus calculator, we can now solve many more binomial distribution problems directly without using a normal approximation, so the methods of this section are not as necessary as they once were. This section is not required for future chapters and may be omitted if time is an issue. *Recommendation:* Omit this section.

Activity: Simulate births by asking each student to toss a coin 25 times. Let outcomes of heads represent females and let tails represent males. Ask each student to announce the number of females and males, then keep a cumulative total. Now address the issue of whether the results are usual or unusual. Important: Ask that students use the normal approximation to the binomial distribution to find the probability of getting the number of females that was obtained, then ask if this is the probability to be used for determining whether the results are unusual. (Answer: No, we need the probability of getting a number of females that is *at least as extreme* as the number obtained.) Proceed to find the probability of getting a number of females *at least as extreme* as the number obtained, then determine whether the results are unusual.

Extra Example: If a gender-selection technique is tested with 500 couples who each have one baby, find the probability of getting at least 275 girls. What would that result suggest? (Answer: 0.0143 or 0.0142 if using technology; because the probability is so small, the result suggests that the gender-selection technique appears to increase the likelihood of a baby being a girl.)

Minimum Outcome Objectives After completing Section 6-6, students should be able to identify conditions for which it is appropriate to use a normal distribution as an approximation to some binomial probability distribution. When it is appropriate, they should be able to use the normal distribution for finding probabilities for a binomial distribution.

Recommended Assignment: Exercises 1-8, 13-20, 30, 32.

6-7 Assessing Normality

Among the topics discussed in the following chapters, some have a loose requirement that the population must have a normal distribution, whereas others have a stricter requirement of normality. For example, Section 7-4 has a requirement that is somewhat loose in the sense that the population distribution need not be exactly normal, but it must have a distribution that is basically symmetric with only one mode. But Section 7-5 has a fairly strict requirement that the population must have a normal distribution. In Section 7-5, substantial departures from a normal distribution can lead to substantial errors. This is why it is important to determine whether we have sample data that are from a normally distributed population.

Recommendation: Stress the *interpretation* of a normal quantile plot, but do not stress the mechanics of actually creating one. On a test, provide displayed results from a technology such as STATDISK, Minitab, Excel, or a TI-83/84 Plus calculator, and ask whether the sample data are from a normally distributed population.

Extra Example: Determine whether the following test scores are normally distributed, and give a reason: 0, 45, 46, 47, 48, 48, 48, 49, 50, 50, 51, 52, 53, 55, 100. (Answer: Because the two values of 0 and 100 are both outliers, there are 2 outliers in a relatively small sample, so the data do not appear to be normally distributed.)

Minimum Outcome Objectives After completing Section 6-7, students should have developed an ability to examine histograms, outliers, and normal quantile plots to determine whether sample data are from a distribution that is approximately normal. They should be able to examine a normal quantile plot and determine whether it depicts data from a normal distribution.

Recommended Assignment: Exercises 1-12. (Exercises 13-16 require the use of technology to generate normal quantile plots.)

Chapter 7

This Chapter is the first introduction to one of the two major activities of inferential statistics: estimating parameters and testing hypotheses. Every introductory statistics course should include at least Sections 7-2 and 7–4, and most include Sections 7-2, 7-3, and 7-4. Section 7-5 can be omitted if there is not sufficient time to include it.

7-2 Estimating a Population Proportion

This section introduces confidence interval estimates of a population proportion p, as well as determining the sample size required to estimate p.

Many textbooks begin with estimates of μ, followed by estimates of p, but this book begins with estimates of p. There are a few good reasons for beginning with p, including these: We continue with one of the last topics of the preceding chapter (normal approximation to binomial); students generally see proportions much more often in the media than they see means. They are very aware of surveys and they have all heard of "margins of error" as they relate to percentages. Students also tend to be more interested in statistics expressed as proportions or percentages. Finally, methods of inferential statistics have fewer complications when proportions are involved than when means are involved. When introducing confidence interval estimates of a parameter for the first time, it would be better to focus on the concepts and methods without being too concerned with complicating factors such as choosing between normal and *t* distributions.

When describing critical values, make the point that they will be used often throughout the remainder of the book, so it is important to understand them now.

Beginning in this section and throughout the remainder of the book, a formal "requirement check" is included in solutions whenever such a check is appropriate. Encourage students to think about such requirement checks, and constantly remind them to question the source of the data, the method used to collect the sample data, the context of the data, and any other relevant factors that might affect the usefulness or validity of results.

Activity: Use the sample proportion of the number of females in the class and construct a 95% confidence interval estimate of the percentage of females in statistics classes. Then discuss whether the sample is good for this purpose. (It is not.)

Extra Example: In the first two months of a recent year, 94 car occupants were killed by air bags, and 61 of them were "improperly belted" (based on data from the National Highway Traffic Safety Administration). Construct a 95% confidence interval estimate of the percentage of car occupants who were killed by air bags while being improperly belted. Based on the results, is it safe to say that the majority of car occupants killed by air bags were improperly belted?
(Answer: $55.2\% < p < 74.5\%$; yes, the confidence interval limits suggest that the percentage is greater than 50%.)

Minimum Outcome Objectives After completing Section 7-2, students should be able to construct a confidence interval estimate of a population proportion and interpret such confidence interval estimates. Students should also be able to identify the requirements necessary for the procedure that is used, and they should be able to determine whether those requirements are satisfied. Students should also be able to determine critical values that correspond to various levels of confidence. Students should be able to determine the sample size necessary to estimate a population proportion.

Recommended Assignment: Exercises 1–14, 21, 22, 25-34, 41, 42. (These exercises require determination of sample size: 25-28, 41-44.) Be sure that students can find critical z values, as in Exercises 5-8.

7-3 Estimating a Population Mean: σ Known

This section discusses estimates of μ, but it is assumed that the population standard deviation σ is known and either the population is normally distributed or $n > 30$, so the normal distribution will be used. Methods for dealing with an unknown σ are discussed in Section 7–4. Because the requirements of this section are somewhat unrealistic, this section could be omitted, but this section does include a practical method for determining sample size when trying to estimate the value of the population mean μ.

Recommendation: If time is becoming an issue, omit this section.

Extra Example: A random sample of 50 movie patrons results in a mean IQ score of 103.0. Assuming that the population standard deviation is known to be 15, construct a 95% confidence interval estimate of the mean IQ of all movie patrons. Can we safely say that movie patrons have a mean IQ score greater than 100? (Answer: $98.8 < \mu < 107.2$; no, the mean is not necessarily greater than 100.)

Minimum Outcome Objectives After completing Section 7-3, students should be able to construct a confidence interval estimate of a population mean when given sample data and a known value of a population standard deviation. They should be able to interpret such confidence interval estimates. Students should also be able to identify the requirements necessary for the procedure that is used, and they should be able to determine whether those requirements are satisfied. Students should also be able to determine critical values that correspond to various levels of confidence. Students should be able to determine the sample size necessary to estimate a population mean.

Recommended Assignment: Exercises 1-14. 17-24. 27-30, 33, 34. (These exercises require the determination of sample size: 17-20, 33-38.)

7-4 Estimating a Population Mean: σ Not Known

It was recommended that Section 7-3 be skipped if time has become an issue, but Section 7-4 is extremely important and should be included. It introduces the important *t* distribution used for constructing confidence interval estimates of a population mean μ. Unlike Section 7-3 that was unrealistic in its requirement of a known population standard deviation σ, this section does not require that σ be known, so the methods are very realistic and are used often.

Comment that the methods of this section require that the parent population has a distribution that is essentially normal (even when the *t* distribution is used) or that $n > 30$.

When estimating μ using sample data with an unknown population standard deviation σ, we use the t distribution (assuming that other requirements are satisfied). (We do not use the normal distribution when $n > 30$, as is done in some textbooks). Professional statisticians almost never take the other approach of using the normal distribution with σ unknown, regardless of the sample size.

If the original population is not normally distributed, the bootstrap method is an interesting alternative, especially for students with great enthusiasm for computers. *Recommendation:* Assign the Technology Project with an oral and written report as an extra-credit assignment.

Activity: Request that each student record his or her pulse rate as the number of beats in one minute. Then proceed to use the sample to construct a 95% confidence interval estimate of the mean pulse rate of all such students. The active involvement of students will increase the likelihood that they better understand and remember the concepts of this section.

Extra Example: A random sample of 15 movie patrons results in a mean IQ score of 103.0 and a standard deviation of 14.7. The 15 IQ scores appear to come from a normally distributed population. Construct a 95% confidence interval estimate of the mean IQ of all movie patrons. Can we safely say that movie patrons have a mean IQ score greater than 100? (Answer: $94.9 < \mu < 111.1$; no, the mean is not necessarily greater than 100.)

Minimum Outcome Objectives After completing Section 7-4, students should be able to construct a confidence interval estimate of a population mean. They should be able to interpret such confidence interval estimates. Students should also be able to identify the requirements necessary for the procedure that is used, and they should be able to determine whether those requirements are satisfied. Students should also be able to determine critical values that correspond to various levels of confidence.

Recommended Assignment: Exercises 1-18, 23, 24.

7-5 Estimating a Population Variance

Many instructors omit this section because of time limitations. The chi-square distribution is introduced here, but it can be introduced in Chapter 8. (Section 8-6 is written so that the chi-square distribution can be introduced there.) Many other instructors feel strongly that the importance of variation requires inclusion of this section. *Recommendation:* If time is an issue, omit this section.

If this section is included, discuss the fact that for a sample with variance s^2 close to the population variance σ^2, the value of χ^2 will be close to the number of degrees of freedom $n - 1$ (because the ratio of s^2/σ^2 will be close to 1). Also discuss the fact that s^2 is positive, σ^2 is positive, and $n - 1$ is positive, so χ^2 will be positive. This explains why the χ^2 graph begins at 0.

Important note about the format of confidence intervals in this section: The format of (0.56, 0.74) is sometimes used instead of $0.56 < \sigma < 0.74$, but any format using $s \pm E$ *cannot* be used because s is not at the center of the confidence interval.

Sample Size Almost every other textbook ignores the topic of determining sample sizes required to estimate σ or σ^2, even after covering sample sizes required for estimating means and proportions. In many cases, the standard deviation is the most important parameter, so its estimation is critically important. That is why sample size determination is included in this section.

Extra Example: A random sample of 15 movie patrons results in a mean IQ score of 103.0 and a standard deviation of 14.7. The 15 IQ scores appear to come from a normally distributed population. Construct a 95% confidence interval estimate of the standard deviation of IQ scores of all movie patrons. (Answer: $10.8 < \sigma < 23.2$)

Minimum Outcome Objectives After completing Section 7-5, students should be able to construct a confidence interval estimate of a population standard deviation or variance, and they should be able to interpret such confidence interval estimates. Students should also be able to identify the requirements necessary for the procedure that is used, and they should be able to determine whether those requirements are satisfied. Students should also be able to determine critical values that correspond to various levels of confidence.

Recommended Assignment: Exercises 1-18, 21, 22. (These exercises require determination of sample size: Exercises 13-16.)

Chapter 8

Instead of beginning the coverage of hypothesis testing with terminology or a sequence of mechanical steps, begin with a big picture *overview* of the basic concept used. Focus on the issue of *significance*: Do the sample results differ from the claim by an amount that is statistically significant? *Recommendation:* Assign Section 8-1 for reading to be completed before this chapter is discussed in class. Consider a quick and easy quiz with a question similar to the one given in the gender selection example in Section 8-1. It involves a clear situation and students can easily understand it. Comment that the actual conclusion depends on the *probability* of getting 52 girls or 97 girls when 100 babies are born. Students have already seen the Rare Event Rule for inferential statistics, and methods of hypothesis testing are built around that rule.

Every introductory statistics course should include at least Sections 8–2, 8–3, and 8–5, and most include Sections 8-2 through 8–5. Section 8–6 can be omitted if there is not sufficient time to include it. The author recommends skipping Section 8-4 because it involves the assumption of a known population standard deviation, which is unrealistic, but many professors feel strongly that Section 8-4 should be included.

Be sure to clearly inform students of what is expected when they conduct hypothesis tests for homework and examinations. *Recommendation:* Require these components:

1. Statements of H_0 and H_1
2. A graph showing the appropriate distribution with the test statistic and either the P–value or the critical value(s) and critical region
3. A statement of either "reject H_0" or "fail to reject H_0"
4. Summary statement of the conclusion, which should be in non–technical terms and it should address the original claim.

Grading Recommendation: When grading a solution to a question requiring a hypothesis test, give equal credit for each of the following:

1. Statements of H_0 and H_1
2. Graph showing the correct distribution (normal, *t*, chi-square, *F*)
3. Correct value of the test statistic
4. Correct P-value or critical value(s)
5. Correct statement of either "reject H_0" or "fail to reject H_0"
6. Correct summary statement of the conclusion

For example, include a hypothesis test question on an exam and assign it 24 points, with 4 points for each of the six items given above.

8-2 Basics of Hypothesis Testing

Section 8-2 is divided into two parts: Part 1 (Basic Concepts of Hypothesis Testing) and Part 2 (Beyond the Basics of Hypothesis Testing: The *Power* of a Test). It is difficult to find the power of a test, so include Part 2 only if you have sufficient time and the topic is suitable for your students.

For notation, note that the null hypothesis will be expressed in terms of *equality* only, so expressions such as $p \leq 0.5$ or $p \geq 0.5$ will not be used for the null hypothesis. (Almost all professional journals use only equality for expressions of null hypotheses.) The notation H_0 is used almost universally, but it is common to see alternative hypotheses expressed as H_1 or H_a. The textbook uses H_1 for alternative hypotheses.

Comment that students will encounter several new terms in this section. These special terms are not unique to this book, or statistics books in general. Instead, these terms are commonly used by medical researchers, manufacturers, psychologists, educators, and many other people who use methods of statistics in their professions. When students learn these terms, they are developing a statistical literacy involving language used in many different disciplines.

Hint for Students: When conducting a test of some hypothesis or claim, it is important to use the correct distribution and the correct expression of the test statistic. Point out that the four different test statistics included in this section are on the detachable Formula/Table card included with the textbook. If students are allowed to use that Formula/Table card on tests, there is no need to memorize formulas. They can simply refer to the card to determine which test statistic is suitable.

P-Values: Section 8-2 includes the traditional method of testing hypotheses, the *P*-value method, and the use of confidence intervals. *Recommendation:* Stress the *P*-value method. *P*-values can usually be found using statistical software or a TI-83/84 Plus calculator, but if students are not using a technology and are using tables in Appendix A instead, it will sometimes be difficult to find *P*-values (especially when using the *t,* chi-square, or *F* distributions). The traditional method will sometimes be easier for those students using only the tables in Appendix A.

Wording of Final Conclusions: Clearly announce a policy of not accepting *only* final conclusions of "reject the null hypothesis" or "fail to reject the null hypothesis," because such statements mean nothing to most people. The final statement should address the original claim, and it should not involve technical terms, such as "null hypothesis." Students typically have some degree of difficulty with the correct statement of final conclusions. Stress that the precise wording of the final conclusion is very important. Differences between terms such as "support" and "fail to reject" are very important. Show how Figure 8-7 can be used to form the wording of the final conclusion. A copy of Figure 8-7 is included with the detachable Formula/Table card. Also, some students have trouble clearly understanding the meaning of "fail to reject the null hypothesis." You might also use "don't reject" instead of "fail to reject."

Extra Example:

a. A newspaper headline consists of the claim that "Most Americans Support Increased Funding for the Space Program." Given the claim, identify the null and alternative hypotheses. (Answer: H_0: $p = 0.5$. H_1: $p > 0.5$.)

b. When testing the claim that $p \neq 0.125$, the test statistic of $z = 2.67$ is obtained. Identify the *P*-value. (Answer: 0.0076.)

c. When testing a claim that $\mu > 75.0$, the *P*-value of 0.1602 is obtained. What should you conclude? (Answer: Fail to reject the null hypothesis. There is not sufficient evidence to support the claim that the mean is greater than 75.0.)

Minimum Outcome Objectives After completing Section 8-2, students should be able to identify the null and alternative hypotheses when given some claim about a population proportion, mean, standard deviation, or variance. They should be able to calculate a test statistic, determine critical values, *P*-values, and state a final conclusion that addresses the original claim.

Recommended Assignment: Even-numbered exercises 2-40. Stress that these exercises involve concepts that will be used again in future sections, so it would be really helpful to take the time to master these concepts now.

8-3 Testing a Claim about a Proportion

This section presents three methods for testing hypotheses: (1) traditional method; (2) *P*-value method; (3) confidence intervals. Again, it is recommended that if you are making extensive use of TI-83/84 Plus calculators or computer software, you might consider emphasizing the *P*-value approach instead of the traditional approach. There is a current trend to make more use of the *P*-value approach. When defining *P*-value, reinforce the importance of getting a value *at least as extreme* as the one found. Refer to Figure 8-8 and suggest that students use it regularly as a basic guide for including all of the steps of a complete hypothesis test.

If you did not cover Section 6-6, point out that under certain circumstances (such as those listed as the three requirements), a binomial distribution can be approximated by a normal distribution. If Section 6-6 was covered, we use a test statistic that does not include the continuity correction from Section 6-6. The continuity correction is not included because its effects tend to be very small with large samples.

Activity: Use the proportion of females in the class to test the claim that "50% of all statistics students are females."

Extra Example: In the first two months of a recent year, 94 car occupants were killed by air bags, and 61 of them were "improperly belted" (based on data from the National Highway Traffic Safety Administration). Use a 0.05 significance level to test the claim that among car occupants killed by air bags, the majority were improperly belted.
(Answer: Test statistic is $z = 2.89$. *P*-value = 0.0019. Critical value is $z = 1.645$. Reject H_0: $p = 0.5$ and support H_1: $p > 0.5$. There is sufficient evidence to support the claim that among car occupants killed by air bags, the majority were "improperly belted.")

Minimum Outcome Objectives After completing Section 8-3, students should be able to conduct a formal hypothesis test of a claim made about a population proportion. The procedure should include statements of the null and alternative hypotheses, determination of the test statistic, critical value(s) or *P*-value, conclusion of rejecting the null hypothesis or failing to reject the null hypothesis, and a final conclusion that addresses the original claim.

Recommended Assignment: Exercises 1-10, 15-18. Note that the directions for Exercises 9-24 stipulate that the *P*–value method should be used "unless your instructor specifies otherwise." The *P*–value method is recommended, but instructors can stipulate that the traditional method be used for some or all of the assigned exercises. Most Appendix E answers include both *P*–values and critical values.

8-4 Testing a Claim about a Mean: σ Known

This section introduces hypothesis tests for claims about a population mean, *assuming that the population standard deviation is known*, so that the normal distribution applies. Comment that in reality, it is very rare to test a claim about μ when the value of the population standard deviation σ is unknown. If pressed for time, this section may be skipped, but Section 8-5 is very important and should not be skipped.

Extra Example: A random sample of 50 movie patrons results in a mean IQ score of 103.0. Assuming that the population standard deviation is known to be 15 and using a 0.05 significance level, test the claim that movie patrons have a mean IQ score equal to 100.
(Answer: Test statistic is $z = 1.41$. *P*-value = 0.1586 or 0.1573 if using technology. Critical values are $z = -1.96$ and 1.96. Fail to reject H_0: $\mu = 100$. There is not sufficient evidence to warrant rejection of the claim that the mean IQ of movie patrons is equal to 100.)

Minimum Outcome Objectives After completing Section 8-4, students should be able to conduct a formal hypothesis test of a claim made about a population mean, assuming that the population standard deviation is known. The procedure should include statements of the null and alternative hypotheses, determination of the test statistic, critical value(s) or *P*-value, conclusion of rejecting the null hypothesis or failing to reject the null hypothesis, and a final conclusion that addresses the original claim.

Recommended Assignment:
Even–numbered Exercises 2–14, and exercises 17 and 18.

8-5 Testing a Claim about a Mean: σ Not Known

This section is extremely important and should definitely be included. This section uses the same *t* distribution introduced in Section 7–4. Also, the criterion for choosing between a normal distribution and a Student *t* distribution are the same in this chapter as they are in Chapter 7. [Two of the top ten textbooks use the normal distribution when $n > 30$, but this book and most others use the t distribution whenever σ is unknown (assuming that the other requirements are satisfied). Professional statisticians almost never use the normal distribution when $n > 30$.]

Activity: Conduct an actual t test in class by using data collected from students in the class. Here is one example: Before class, measure your own pulse rate. In class, ask each student to measure his or her pulse rate as the number of beats in one minute. Proceed to test the claim that the class has a mean pulse rate different from yours. The active involvement will provide a better learning experience.

Recommendation: If your students are using TI-83/84 Plus calculators or statistical software, encourage use of the P-value approach to hypothesis testing, but if they are using only the tables in Appendix A, allow them to use the traditional method.

Extra Example: A random sample of 15 movie patrons results in a mean IQ score of 103.0 and a standard deviation of 14.7. The sample of IQ scores appears to come from a population with a normal distribution. Use a 0.05 significance level to test the claim that the mean IQ score of movie patrons is greater than 100.
(Answer: Test statistic is $t = 0.790$. P-value = 0.2212. Critical value is $t = 1.761$. Fail to reject H_0: $\mu = 100$. There is not sufficient evidence to support H_1: $\mu > 100$. There is not sufficient evidence to support the claim that the mean IQ of movie patrons is greater than 100.)

Minimum Outcome Objectives After completing Section 8-5, students should be able to conduct a formal hypothesis test of a claim made about a population mean. The procedure should include statements of the null and alternative hypotheses, determination of the test statistic, critical value(s) or P-value, conclusion of rejecting the null hypothesis or failing to reject the null hypothesis, and a final conclusion that addresses the original claim.

Recommended assignment: Exercises 1–16, 23-26. The directions for Exercises 17-32 state that unless stipulated by the instructor, either the traditional method or P–value method can be used, so be sure to indicate a preference if you have one.

8-6 Testing a Claim about Variation

This section can be easily omitted if time is an issue. If Section 7-5 was omitted but this section is to be covered, be sure to describe the χ^2 distribution, because this will be the first time that students see it.

After covering this section, students will have studied three different parameters (p, μ, σ) along with three different distributions (normal, t, χ^2). Point out that the detachable Formula/Table card includes test statistics, and the form of the test statistic often reveals the distribution that should be used. For example, the Formula/Table card shows that the test statistic for a claim involving the standard deviation or variance is $\chi^2 = (n - 1)s^2/\sigma^2$, so this test statistic indicates that the χ^2 distribution is used. There is no need to memorize test statistic formulas, so students can focus on more important concepts.

Recommendation: If your students are using statistical software, encourage use of the *P*-value approach to hypothesis testing, but if they are using only the tables in Appendix A, allow them to use the traditional method.

Extra Example: A random sample of 15 movie patrons results in a mean IQ score of 103.0 and a standard deviation of 14.7. The sample of IQ scores is from a population having a normal distribution. Use a 0.05 significance level to test the claim that IQ scores of movie patrons have a standard deviation less than 20.
(Answer: Test statistic is $\chi^2 = 7.563$. *P*-value = 0.0892. Critical value is $\chi^2 = 6.571$. Fail to reject H_0: $\chi^2 = 20$. There is not sufficient evidence to support H_1: $\chi^2 < 20$. There is not sufficient evidence to support the claim that the movie patrons have IQ scores with a standard deviation less than 20.)

Minimum Outcome Objectives After completing Section 8-6, students should be able to conduct a formal hypothesis test of a claim made about a population standard deviation or variance. The procedure should include statements of the null and alternative hypotheses, determination of the test statistic, critical value(s) or *P*-value, conclusion of rejecting the null hypothesis or failing to reject the null hypothesis, and a final conclusion that addresses the original claim.

Recommended Assignment: Exercises 1-8, 11-14.

Chapter 9

Some instructors cover all of Chapter 9 while many others omit it because they don't have enough time. Even if this chapter is not discussed in class, strongly consider assigning some exercises from it. Once students understand the basic concepts of hypothesis testing and confidence intervals (from Chapters 7 and 8), they can use software or a TI-83/84 Plus calculator to do the number crunching, then they can focus on the interpretation of the results. Also, there is a real pedagogical advantage in teaching confidence intervals in Chapter 7 and hypothesis testing in Chapter 8, then having students independently apply the same general concepts to different circumstances included in this chapter.

Sections 9-2, 9-3 and 9-4 are especially important, so consider covering those sections or at least assigning some exercises from them.

9-2 Inferences about Two Proportions

Finding the Numbers of Successes x_1 and x_2 Many students experience difficulty finding the actual number of successes from a statement such as this: "When 1125 people are surveyed, 47% of them said that they fly never or rarely." A brief review of the procedure for finding the number of successes can help remove that obstacle. Also, be sure to assign Exercises 5-8, which deal with this issue.

Point out that the concept of a pooled estimate of proportions applies only to cases in which we assume that $p_1 = p_2$. If we do not assume that $p_1 = p_2$, as in the construction of a confidence interval for their difference, we do not use a pooled estimate of proportions.

Extra Example: In a study of 1700 teens aged 15–19, half were given written surveys and half were given surveys using an anonymous computer program. Among those given the written surveys, 67 (or 7.9%) say that they carried a gun within the last 30 days. Among those given the computer surveys, 105 (or 12.4%) say that they carried a gun within the last 30 days (based on data from the Urban Institute).

a. The sample percentages of 7.9% and 12.4% are obviously not equal, but is the difference significant? Explain. (Answer: Test statistic is $z = -3.06$. P-value = 0.0022. Critical values are $z = -1.96$ and 1.96, assuming a 0.05 significance level. Reject H_0: $p_1 = p_2$. There is sufficient evidence to support the claim that there is a significant different between the two percentages.)

b. Construct a 99% confidence interval estimate of the difference between the two population percentages, and interpret the result.
(Answer: $-8.23\% < p_1 - p_2 < -0.71\%$ or $0.71\% < p_1 - p_2 < 8.23\%$)

Minimum Outcome Objectives After completing Section 9-2, students should be able to conduct a formal hypothesis test of a claim made about two population proportions. They should also be able to construct a confidence interval estimate of the difference between two population proportions.

Recommended Assignment: Exercises 1-16, 21, 22

9-3 Inferences about Two Means: Independent Samples

This section has been partitioned into Parts 1 and 2. Part 1 involves situations in which the standard deviations of the two populations are unknown and are not assumed to be equal. Part 2 involves two other situations: (1) The two population standard deviations are both known; (2) the two population standard deviations are unknown but are assumed to be equal. *Recommendation:* Cover Part 1 and skip Part 2.

Activity: Use the measured pulse rates from the class to test for a difference between the mean pulse rate of men and the mean pulse rate of women. Again, the active involvement will enhance their learning experience. It will also ensure that all students are awake and alive.

Point out that a common objective in constructing a *confidence interval* estimate of the difference $\mu_1 - \mu_2$ is to determine whether the confidence interval limits contain 0. If those limits do contain 0, then there is not a significant difference between the two sample means, which suggests that the two population means are equal. If those limits do not contain 0, then it appears that the two population means are different. Because the hypothesis test and confidence interval use the same distribution and standard error, they are equivalent in the sense that they result in the same conclusions.

Extra Example: As part of the National Health Survey, data were collected on the weights of men in two different age brackets. For 804 men aged 25–34, the mean is 176 lb and the standard deviation is 35.0 lb. For 1657 men aged 65–74, the mean and standard deviation are 164 lb and 27.0 lb, respectively.

a. Test the claim that the older men come from a population with a mean that is less than the mean for men in the 25–34 age bracket. Use a 0.01 significance level. (Answer: Test statistic is $t = 8.564$. Critical value: $t = 2.331$ (approximately). *P*-value: 0.0001 or 0.0000 if using technology. Reject H_0: $\mu_1 = \mu_2$. There is sufficient evidence to support the claim that the older men come from a population with a mean that is less than the mean for the younger men.)

b. Construct a 99% confidence interval for the difference between the means of the men in the two age brackets. Do the confidence interval limits contain 0? Does this indicate that there is or is not a significant difference between the two means? (Answer: $8.4 < \mu_1 - \mu_2 < 15.6$; no; there does appear to be a significant difference between the two means.)

Minimum Outcome Objectives After completing Section 9-3, students should be able to distinguish between a situation involving two independent samples and a situation involving two samples that are not independent. They should be able to conduct a formal hypothesis test of a claim made about two means from independent populations. They should also be able to construct a confidence interval estimate of the difference between two population means.

Recommended Assignment: Exercises 1–14

9-4 Inferences from Matched Pairs

Warn students against blindly using the methods of this section whenever they have paired data. For example, suppose we have pulse rates of students matched with their heights. Even though the data are paired, it would make no sense to apply the methods of this section. Such data might be analyzed using methods of correlation and regression, but we should not conduct any analysis based on differences between pulse rates and heights. It makes no sense to find the difference between an individual's pulse rate and his or her height. We should constantly warn students against blind use of formulas or procedures. We should always *think* about what we are doing.

Activity: Have students measure their pulse rates (or recall it from a previous class), then ask them to again measure their pulse rates after standing for one minute. Each student should have a matched data consisting of a sitting pulse rate and a standing pulse rate. Now use the data from the class to test the claim that the differences have a mean equal to 0.

Extra Example: In low-speed crash tests of five BMW cars, the repair costs were computed for a factory-authorized repair center and an independent repair facility. The results are listed in the accompanying table.

Authorized repair center	$797	$571	$904	$1147	$418
Independent repair center	$523	$488	$875	$911	$297

a. Is there sufficient evidence to support the claim that the independent center has lower repair costs? Use a 0.01 significance level.
(Answer: Test statistic: $t = 3.215$. Critical value: $t = 3.747$. P-value = 0.0162). Fail to reject H_0: $\mu_d = 0$. There is not sufficient evidence to support the claim that the independent center has lower repair costs.)

b. Construct a 99% confidence interval estimate of the mean difference between the repair costs of the factory-authorized repair center and the independent repair center. Do the confidence interval limits contain 0?
(Answer: $-64.2 < \mu_d < 361.4$; yes)

Minimum Outcome Objectives After completing Section 9-4, students should be able to identify sample data consisting of matched pairs. They should be able to conduct a formal hypothesis test of a claim made about the mean of the differences between matched pairs. They should also be able to construct a confidence interval estimate of the mean difference between matched pairs.

Recommended Assignment: Exercises 1–6, 9-14.

9-5 Comparing Variation in Two Samples

If time is an issue, this section can be omitted. If this section is covered, really stress that the methods of this section have a very *strict* requirement of a normally distributed population. Departures from normality can result in very poor results. See the listed requirements in the textbook.

The basic method of this section involves making s_1^2 the *larger* variance, so that we can avoid the tricky problem of finding critical F values for left-tailed cases. Note, however, that the distribution of s_1^2 / s_2^2 is the F distribution illustrated in Figure 9-5 only if we haven't yet imposed the condition that s_1^2 is the larger of the two sample variances. (Once we impose that condition, the ratio of s_1^2 / s_2^2 must be 1 or greater.)

There will be questions about finding critical values when the number of degrees of freedom is not one of those found in Table A-5. We can usually use the nearest values; it usually doesn't make a difference if we use the value above or below the desired missing value. It only makes a difference if the test statistic is between the table values, in which case you could interpolate, but it's best to run the problem using software or a TI-83/84 Plus calculator.

Alternative Methods The subsection labeled "Alternative Methods" is new to this edition. Only Exercises 21 and 22 (Beyond the Basics) relate to these alternative methods, and the content of this subsection could be assigned for independent reading or could be omitted.

Activity: If the pulse rates of students were collected in some previous activity, it would be easy to test the null hypothesis that males and females have pulse rates with the same variation. However, before conducting the hypothesis test, set a good example and explore the data to verify the requirements, especially the requirement of normally distributed data.

Extra Example: Given the sample data below, use a 0.05 significance level to test the claim that the treatment population and the placebo population have different variances.

Treatment group: $n = 11$, $\bar{x} = 12.6$, $s = 2.8$
Placebo group: $n = 15$, $\bar{x} = 12.9$, $s = 1.8$

(Answer: Test statistic is $F = 2.4198$. Right critical value is $F = 3.1469$. P-value = 0.1277. Fail to reject H_0: $\sigma_1^2 = \sigma_2^2$. There is not sufficient evidence to support the claim that the two populations have different variances.)

Minimum Outcome Objectives After completing Section 9-5, students should be able to conduct a formal hypothesis test of a claim made about two population standard deviations or variances.

Recommended Assignment: Exercises 1–12

Chapter 10

Some instructors prefer to cover the basics of correlation/regression early in their course. Sections 10-2 and 10-3 are organized and written so that they can follow Chapter 3. If covering Sections 10-2 and 10-3 early in the course, simply cover Part 1 in Section 10-2 and cover Part 1 in Section 10-3; exclude Part 2 in each of those sections.

Minimum coverage of this chapter should include linear correlation and regression, as discussed in Sections 10-2 and 10-3, which are not very difficult. The multiple regression of Section 10-5 and modeling in Section 10-6 emphasize the use of technology.

10-2 Correlation

Begin by making the important point that the *context* of data is extremely important. The context can dramatically affect the methods we use. Show an unidentified table of values, such as this one:

x	78	85	92	100	85
y	89	93	99	100	84

Ask these questions:

1. What is the key issue if these data are test grades of subjects before and after formal instruction? ("Is the instruction effective, as indicated by higher y scores?" See Section 9-4.)

2. What is the key issue if these data are reasoning tests for a sample of men (x) and a separate sample of women (y)? ("Does the population of men have the same mean as the population of women?" See Section 9-3.)

3. What is the key issue if each pair represents a math reasoning score x and a starting salary y in thousands of dollars? ("Is the starting salary associated with math reasoning?" See this chapter.)

Part 2: Formal Hypothesis Test As the title of this subsection indicates, this material requires prior coverage of Chapter 8. If you are including Sections 10-2 and 10-3 early (such as following Chapter 3), skip this subsection. If you do include this subsection, be sure to inform the class that you prefer Method 1 or Method 2. There are pros and cons for both methods, but the author recommends Method 2 because it is generally easier.

Finding r The manual calculation of the linear correlation coefficient r is messy. *Recommendation:* Demonstrate the calculation of r in class by doing the following activity, but encourage students to find r by using a calculator or statistical software. They should be encouraged to focus on understanding and interpreting values of r, not performing arithmetic calculations with a formula.

Activity: Consider doing an in-class example with six pairs of data. Randomly select six students and use their pulse rates and heights. Show the scatterplot and the calculation of r using Formula 10-1. Suggestion: Demonstrate the manual calculation of r, but then move on and assume that values of r will be found by using calculators or software. This reflects the trend in introductory statistics courses: Require less number crunching and more thinking, analysis, and interpretation.

Extra Example: Many of us have heard that a tip should be 15% of the bill. The accompanying table lists some sample data collected from the author's students. Is there sufficient evidence to conclude that there is a relationship between the amount of the bill and the amount of the tip?

Bill ($)	33.46	50.68	87.92	98.84	63.60	107.34
Tip ($)	5.50	5.00	8.08	17.00	12.00	16.00

(Answer: $r = 0.828$. Critical values are $r = -0.811$ and $r = 0.811$, assuming a 0.05 significance level. P-value = 0.0418. Reject H_0: $\rho = 0$. There is sufficient evidence to support the claim that there is a relationship between the amount of the bill and the amount of the tip.)

Minimum Outcome Objectives After completing Section 10-2, students should be able to use paired data to find the value of the linear correlation coefficient *r*, and determine whether the result leads to the conclusion that there is a linear correlation between two variables.

Recommended Assignment: Exercises 1–6, 11- 14, 21, 22, 25, 33-36

10-3 Regression

Note that Section 10-3 is partitioned into Part 1 (Basic Concepts of Regression) and Part 2 (Beyond the Basics of Regression). Skip Part 2 if time is an issue.

Begin by briefly reviewing the $y = mx + b$ format of the equation of a straight line:

1. What does m represent?
2. What does b represent?
3. What if the equation is changed to a format of $y = b_0 + b_1x$? What is the slope? What is the y-intercept?

Finding the Regression Equation Once again, you must decide what you require from students. *Recommendation:* Illustrate the use of Formulas 10-2 and 10-3 once, but then allow students to find the slope and intercept from their calculators or statistical software. This is consistent with the trend of making the statistics course much more meaningful than laboriously cranking out formula values.

Students typically experience some difficulty in determining the best predicted value of a variable. Begin by randomly selecting a student and asking him or her to predict the IQ of a male who is 6 ft tall, then explain why the answer of 100 makes sense. (There is no correlation between IQ and height, and the answer of 100 is not based on any regression equation.) Now randomly select another student and ask him or her to predict the time it would take to drive 100 miles. Answers such as two or three hours are good, and they involve a calculation using an estimated regression equation.

Activity: Use the class to collect sample paired data, then find the regression equation. Avoid using any measurements that might embarrass someone, such as weight. Consider the first Cooperative Group Activity given near the end of Chapter 10 in the textbook. It involves measures of height and "naval height" and verification of an old theory about the association between those two variables.

Extra Example: Many of us have heard that the tip should be 15% of the bill. The accompanying table lists some sample data collected from the author's students. Assuming that there is a linear correlation between the amount of the bill and the amount of the tip, find the equation that could be used for determining the amount of the tip that should be left.

Bill ($)	33.46	50.68	87.92	98.84	63.60	107.34
Tip ($)	5.50	5.00	8.08	17.00	12.00	16.00

(Answer: $y = -0.347 + 0.149x$, where y represents the tip. That is, leave 35 cents less than 14.9% of the bill. Or leave about 15% of the bill.)

Minimum Outcome Objectives After completing Section 10-3, students should be able to use paired sample data to determine the equation of the regression line. They should have developed the ability to find the best predicted value of a variable given some value of another variable.

Recommended Assignment: Exercises 1–6, 11-14, 21, 22, 25

10-4 Variation and Prediction Intervals

The calculations in this section will seriously challenge students without software or calculators capable of dealing with two-variable statistics. The manual calculation of the value of s_e is challenging, but this statistic is important enough to be included among the values provided by STATDISK, Minitab, Excel, and the TI-83/84 Plus calculator. If you choose to cover this section, but students do not have statistical software or a TI-83/84 Plus calculator, consider providing them with displays from technology. The students can then focus on interpreting the displays or using results from them.

Extra Example: Refer to the Table 10-1 sample data in the textbook. Let x represent the duration time (in seconds) and let y represent the time interval (in minutes) after the eruption to the next eruption. Use a duration time of $x = 150$ sec to construct a 95% prediction interval estimate of the time interval after the eruption to the next eruption. (Answer: 55.4 min $< y <$ 84.4 min.)

Minimum Outcome Objectives After completing Section 10-4, students should be able to use paired sample data to determine the value of the coefficient of determination r^2, and to interpret that value. They should be able to use paired sample data to use a given value of the predictor value to find a prediction interval for the other variable.

Recommended Assignment: Exercises 1–14, 17, 18. (Exercises 1-12 are quick and easy.)

10-5 Multiple Regression

Because the formulas required for manual calculations of multiple regression equations are formidable, this section emphasizes computer usage and interpretation of computer results. This section can be covered even if students do not have access to suitable software; simply assign only those exercises that include computer displays. Some instructors include this section by assigning exercises as extra-credit or out-of-class work.

If time is limited, the subsection of "Dummy Variables and Logistic Regression" can be easily omitted.

Activity: Ideally, demonstrate the statistical software or TI-83/84 Plus calculator that is being used by the class. Either collect sample data from the class or use one of the data sets in Appendix B. For example, randomly and *anonymously* select several students from the class roster, then use the numbers of absences and grades on the first test to predict grades on the second test.

Extra Example: Use the Minitab display. Is the multiple regression equation good for making predictions? Why or why not?

```
The regression equation is

WEIGHT = 2285 + 21.38AGE + 211.2HEADWDTH   + 128.6NECK

Predictor       Coef       Stdev     t-ratio         p
Constant     2285.21       78.45       23.64     0.022
AGE          21.3838      0.9022       21.53     0.200
HEADWDTH      211.24       20.88       20.54     0.619
NECK          28.594       5.870        4.87     0.008

s = 32.49       R-sq = 96.9%    R-sq(adj) = 94.6%

Analysis of Variance

SOURCE       DF         SS         MS        F       p
Regression    3     132425      44142    41.81   0.002
Error         4       4223       1056
Total         7     136648

SOURCE       DF     SEQ SS
AGE           1      90527
HEADWDTH      1      16844
NECK          1      25054
```

(Answer: Yes. The overall significance of 0.002 is low, indicating significance. The adjusted R^2 of 0.946 is very high.)

Minimum Outcome Objectives After completing Section 10-5, students should be able to interpret results from statistical software or TI-83/84 Plus calculators to determine whether a multiple regression equation is suitable for making predictions. They should be able to compare results from different combinations of predictor variables and identify the combination of predictor variables that results in the best multiple regression equation.

Recommended Assignment: Exercises 1-12. (Exercises 1–12 do not require software, but Exercises 13-16 do require software.)

10-6 Modeling

If time is an issue, omit this section. This section requires access to some form of technology. A TI-83/84 Plus calculator is ideal, but STATDISK, Minitab, or Excel can also be used. See the comments in the "Using Technology" box at the end of this section.

Recommendation: Omit this section, but assign exercises as extra-credit work, especially for those students with backgrounds that include more extensive mathematics courses.

Extra Example: Find the model that best fits the paired data given below. Explain why it fits best. (Answer: The quadratic model $y = 3x^2 + 8$ fits best because $R^2 = 1$, which is higher than R^2 for the other models.)

x	1	2	5	6	8	10
y	11	20	83	116	200	308

Minimum Outcome Objectives After completing Section 10-6, students should be able to use paired data to identify the linear, quadratic, logarithmic, exponential, and power models. They should be able to determine which model fits best.

Recommended Assignment: Exercises 1-10

Chapter 11

Coverage of at least Section 11-3 is strongly recommended if time is available for it. Analysis of survey results often involves the use of contingency tables, so the concepts of Section 11-3 are used frequently in real applications. Both Sections 11-2 and 11-3 require the χ^2 distribution, so if it has not yet been introduced, be sure to provide a description of it. Basic concepts of the χ^2 distribution are included here as well as in Section 7–5 and again in Section 8–6.

11-2 Multinomial Experiments: Goodness-of-Fit

Begin by reviewing *expected value*, introduced in Section 5-2. Present a few simple and obvious examples such as this one: Find the expected number of girls born in groups of 100 babies. When students respond with the correct answer of 50, ask them to describe the exact thought process that led to the answer. They will respond that they found 1/2 of 100, which can be generalized as $p \times n$, which leads to $E = np$. Also point out that the expected number of girls among 3 babies is 1.5, so the expected value need not be an integer.

Also, emphasize that the methods of this section require that each *expected frequency* must be at least 5, but there is no requirement that *observed frequencies* must be at least 5.

Lead the class to a development of their own reasoning process for why the tests of this section are all right-tailed. Ask the class these questions: If there are large discrepancies between the observed frequencies and those that are expected, what do we know about the values of $O - E$? The $(O - E)^2$ values? The value of the χ^2 test statistic? Where on the χ^2 distribution do large discrepancies fall?

Activity: Bring in a newspaper with stock prices and collect a sample of their leading digits, then test the claim that those leading digits follow Benford's law. This example will also highlight the procedure for dealing with the more difficult cases in which the expected frequencies are not all the same.

Extra Example: A study was made of 147 industrial accidents that required medical attention. Among those accidents, 31 occurred on Monday, 42 on Tuesday, 18 on Wednesday, 25 on Thursday, and 31 on Friday (based on results from "Counted Data CUSUM's," by Lucas, *Technometrics,* Vol. 27, No. 2). Use a 0.05 significance level to test the claim that accidents occur with equal proportions on the five workdays. (Answer: Test statistic is χ^2 = 10.653. Critical value: χ^2 = 9.488, assuming a 0.05 significance level. *P*-value = 0.0308. Reject the null hypothesis that the frequencies fit a uniform distribution. The accidents do not appear to occur with equal proportions of the five workdays.)

Minimum Outcome Objectives After completing Section 11-2, students should be able to use data separated into different categories and determine whether the data fit some claimed distribution. That is, they should be able to conduct a formal goodness-of-fit hypothesis test.

Recommended Assignment: Exercises 1–7, 10, 18-20

11-3 Contingency Tables: Independence and Homogeneity

The methods of this section are used often in the analysis of survey results. When selecting the topics to be included in the introductory statistics course, this section should be given a reasonably high priority. However, if inclusion of this section meant that there would be no time for such important activities as group projects, then this topic should not be included.

The test statistic given in this section is the same as the one given in Section 11-2. The hypothesis tests of this section are all right-tailed, as in Section 11-2. Differences between this section and Section 11-2 are found in the method used for finding expected values *E* and the calculation of the number of degrees of freedom.

Expected Value E Instead of simply presenting the formula for the calculation of expected value *E*, strongly consider discussing the rationale for that expression. Refer to Table 11-4 and ask the class these questions "in the spirit of reviewing a few of the important and basic principles of probabilities:"

1. If one of the motorcycle drivers is randomly selected, find the probability of getting one who was not injured.

2. Find the probability of getting someone who wore a black helmet.

3. Find the probability of getting a driver who was not injured and wore a black helmet, assuming that being injured is *independent* of the helmet color.

Fisher Exact Test The discussion about the Fisher exact test is provided for relevant information, but the exercises use the methods already discussed in this section. This subsection can be easily omitted. (The newest version of STATDISK now includes the Fisher exact test.)

Activity: This activity is similar to the one for Section 11-2. Bring in a newspaper and use its financial pages for stock prices from two different exchanges, such as the New York Stock Exchange and NASDAQ. Use the leading digits of stock prices from the two different exchanges to construct a two-way table, then use the methods of this section to test the claim that the leading digits are independent of the exchange.

Extra Example: In the judicial case *United States* v. *City of Chicago,* fair employment practices were challenged. A minority group (group A) and a majority group (group B) took the Fire Captain Examination. Assume that the study began with predetermined sample sizes of 24 minority candidates (Group A) and 562 majority candidates (Group B), with the results as shown in the table. At the 0.05 significance level, test the claim that the proportion of minority candidates who pass is the same as the proportion of majority candidates who pass. Based on the results, does the test appear to discriminate?

	Pass	Fail
Group A	10	14
Group B	417	145

(Answer: Test statistic is $\chi^2 = 12.321$. Critical value is $\chi^2 = 3.841$. *P*-value = 0.0004. There is sufficient evidence to warrant rejection of the claim that the proportion of minority candidates who pass is the same as the proportion of majority candidates who pass. The test does appear to discriminate.)

Minimum Outcome Objectives After completing Section 11-3, students should be able to use categorical data summarized as frequencies in a table with a least two rows and at least two columns to conduct a formal test of independence between the row variable and column variable. They should also be able to conduct a formal test of a claim that different populations have the same proportions of some characteristics.

Recommended Assignment: Exercises 1–8, 10-12, 19, 20

11-4 McNemar's Test for Matched Pairs

Section 11-4 is new to this edition. It can be easily omitted if there are time constraints. There are two extremely important points to stress about the methods of this section:

1. The entries in a table such as Table 11-7 in the textbook are frequency counts of *subjects,* not the individual items that constitute pairs. For example, Table 11-8 lists data for 80 subjects having a total of 160 feet, but the sum of the entries in Table 11-8 is 80, not 160.

2. The calculations are based on frequencies for the two *discordant* cases only. (Carefully discuss *discordant* cases. They are the categories in which the two factors are different.)

Extra Example: Subjects are inflicted with athlete's foot on each of their feet and, for each subject, one foot is treated with a fungicide solution while the other foot is "treated" with a placebo. The results are given in the accompanying table. Using a 0.05 significance level, test the effectiveness of the treatment.

		Fungicide Treatment	
		Cure	No cure
Placebo	Cure	18	27
	No cure	14	23

(Answer: Test statistic is $\chi^2 = 3.512$. Critical value is $\chi^2 = 3.841$. *P*-value = 0.061. There is not sufficient evidence to warrant rejection of the null hypothesis that the following two proportions are the same: (1) The proportion of subjects with no cure on the Fungicide-treated foot and a cure on the foot treated with a placebo; (2) the proportion of subjects with a cure on the Fungicide-treated foot and no cure on the foot treated with a placebo. The Fungicide treatment does not appear to be effective.)

Minimum Outcome Objectives After completing Section 11-4, students should be able to use matched pairs of categorical data summarized as frequencies in a table with two rows and two columns to apply McNemar's test for conducting a formal test of the claim that the discordant categories occur in the same proportion. Students should also be able to define *discordant* pairs of categories and determine whether two pairs of categories are discordant.

Recommended Assignment: Exercises 1-12, 15, 16

Chapter 12

Begin by noting that due to the nature of the calculations, this chapter emphasizes the interpretation of displays from software or a TI-83/84 Plus calculator. This chapter can be covered without actually using any particular technology; simply use the exercises that already provide the displayed results.

The recommended teaching strategy involves the interpretation of computer displays along with an understanding of basic theory by considering cases involving samples with the same number of values. The textbook suggests this strategy:

1. Understand that a small *P*-value (such as 0.05 or less) leads to rejection of the null hypothesis of equal means. With a large *P*-value (such as greater than 0.05), fail to reject the null hypothesis of equal means.

2. Develop an understanding of the underlying rationale by studying the examples in this section.

3. Become acquainted with the nature of the SS (sum of squares) and MS (mean square) values and their role in determining the *F* test statistic, but use statistical software packages or a calculator for finding those values.

12-2 One-Way ANOVA

Even if making extensive use of technology, a basic understanding of underlying principles is important. Carefully explain the content of the "Rationale" subsection. *Recommendation:* Unless sufficient time is available, discuss only the case of equal sample sizes, and omit reference to calculations with unequal sample sizes.

The subsection of *Identifying the Means that Are Different* is new to this edition. It is intended mainly for information purposes and can be easily omitted if there are time constraints. If this subsection is discussed, note that Exercise 18 refers to the Tukey test, and Exercise 19 refers to the Bonferroni test, but both exercises have displayed results.

Activity: (See the second Cooperative Group Activity.) First, partition the students into three or four groups according to major or type of major (such as liberal arts, math or science, history or economics, and "other"). Then ask each student to estimate the length of the classroom. Collect the estimates and group them according to the different categories, then use ANOVA to test the claim that the different groups will produce estimates with the same mean.

Extra Example: The accompanying table lists the body temperatures of five randomly selected subjects from each of three different age groups. Use a 0.05 significance level to test the claim that the three age-group populations have the same mean body temperature.

Body Temperatures (ºF) Categorized by Age

18–20	21–29	30 and older
98.0	99.6	98.6
98.4	98.2	98.6
97.7	99.0	97.0
98.5	98.2	97.5
97.1	97.9	97.3

(Answer: Test statistic is $F = 1.88$. Critical value is $F = 3.8853$. P-value = 0.1949. Fail to reject H_0: $\mu_1 = \mu_2 = \mu_3$. There is not sufficient evidence to warrant rejection of the claim that the three age-group populations have the same mean body temperature.)

Minimum Outcome Objectives After completing Section 12-2, students should be able to conduct a hypothesis test of equality of three or more population means by interpreting results from statistical software or a TI-83/84 Plus calculator.

Recommended Assignment: Exercises 1-10. (None of Exercises 1–10 require the use of software or a TI-83/84 Plus calculator. Exercises 11-16 require the use of technology.) If students are using Minitab, their results might not be as precise as answers given in the back of the book. A student might use Minitab to get a test statistic of $F = 15.81$, whereas the answer in the back of the book might be $F = 15.8142$. We recommend informing students that they shouldn't be concerned about those last digits unless the test statistic is very close to the critical value - a condition that is very rare.

12-3 Two-Way ANOVA

This section is not as challenging as it might seem, because it stresses the interpretation of displays obtained from software or a TI-83/84 calculator. This section can be easily omitted if there are time constraints.

Extra Example: Twelve different 4-cylinder cars were tested for highway fuel consumption (in mi/gal) after being driven under identical highway conditions; the results are listed in the table and accompanying Minitab display.

a. At the 0.05 significance level, test the claim that fuel consumption is not affected by an *interaction* between engine size and transmission type.
b. Assume that fuel consumption is not affected by an interaction between engine size and type of transmission. Use a 0.05 level of significance to test the claim that fuel consumption is not affected by engine size.
c. Assume that fuel consumption is not affected by an interaction between engine size and type of transmission. Use a 0.05 level of significance to test the claim that fuel consumption is not affected by type of transmission.

```
Analysis of Variance for MPG
Source          DF        SS        MS        F         P
Transmis         1      40.3      40.3     3.56     0.108
Engine           2      43.2      21.6     1.90     0.229
Interaction      2       1.2       0.6     0.05     0.950
Error            6      68.0      11.3
Total           11     152.7
```

	Engine Size (liters)		
	1.5	2.2	2.5
Automatic Transmission	31, 32	28, 26	31, 23
Manual Transmission	33, 36	33, 30	27, 34

(Answer:
a. Test statistic: F = 0.05. Critical value: F = 5.1433. P-value = 0.950. Fuel consumption does not appear to be affected by an interaction between transmission type and engine size.
b. Test statistic: F = 1.90. Critical value: F = 5.1433. P-value = 0.229. The size of the engine does not appear to have an effect on fuel consumption.
c. Test statistic: F = 3.56. Critical value: F = 5.9874. P-value = 0.108. The type of transmission does not appear to have an effect on fuel consumption.)

Minimum Outcome Objectives After completing Section 12-3, students should be able to apply the method of two-way analysis of variance to (1) test for an interaction between two factors, (2) test for an effect from the row factor, and (3) test for an effect from the column factor. The hypothesis tests can be conducted by interpreting results from statistical software or a TI-83/84 Plus calculator, and the sample data are categorized into groups using two factors.

Recommended Assignment: Exercises 1-12. (Exercises 1–12 do not require the use of software or a TI-83/84 Plus calculator. Assign Exercises 13 and 14 if students have access to technology capable of working with two-way ANOVA, such as STATDISK, Minitab, Excel, or a TI-83/84 Plus calculator.)

Chapter 13

If there are issues with the availability of time, this chapter can be omitted, but it does include some very important and practical topics.

This chapter can be covered separately as one category of procedures devoted to nonparametric methods, or individual sections of this chapter can be covered along with the related parametric methods found in the preceding chapters. Here is a guide that relates the nonparametric methods of this chapter to the corresponding parametric methods.

Nonparametric	↔ Parametric
13-2, 13-3	↔ 9-4
13-4	↔ 9-3
13-5	↔ 12-2
13-6	↔ 10-2

13-2 Sign Test

Point out that the sign test procedure is summarized in the flowchart of Figure 13-1 in the textbook. The sign test deals with sample data that are matched pairs. Matched pairs are also considered in Section 9-4, but the procedure used in that section requires that if the number of pairs of sample data is small ($n \leq 30$), then the population of differences in the paired values must be approximately *normally distributed.* This section has no such requirement of a normal or any other particular distribution.

Tricky Point Try to carefully discuss and clarify a very important component of Figure 13-1 in the textbook: the decision diamond that includes the question "Do the sample data contradict H_1?" Stress that although the flowchart might make it appear that the procedure is automatic, it is important to *think* about the sample data and the claim being tested. If the sample data *contradict* the alternative hypothesis H_1, then fail to reject the null hypothesis and there is no need to actually do a formal sign test. For example, you need not formally test a claim that a coin favors heads if 100 tosses result in 48 heads. There is no way that we could ever support the claim of heads being favored if we get heads in fewer than 50% of the trials.

Activity: (This same activity was suggested for Section 9-4.) Have students measure their pulse rates (or recall it from a previous class), then ask them to again measure their pulse rates after standing for one minute. Each student should have a pair of matched data consisting of a sitting pulse rate and a standing pulse rate. Now use the data from the class to test the claim that the differences have a mean equal to 0.

Extra Example: In low-speed crash tests of five BMW cars, the repair costs were computed for a factory-authorized repair center and an independent repair facility. The results are listed in the accompanying table. Use the sign test with a 0.05 significance level to test the claim that the paired values have differences with a median equal to 0.

Authorized repair center	\$797	\$571	\$904	\$1147	\$418	\$1442
Independent repair center	\$523	\$488	\$875	\$911	\$297	\$898

(Answer: Test statistic is $x = 0$. Critical value is 0. Reject the null hypothesis that the median of the differences is equal to 0. There appears to be a significant difference between the costs from the two repair facilities.)

Minimum Outcome Objectives After completing Section 13-2, students should be able to conduct a sign test for claims involving matched pairs of sample data, or claims involving nominal data, or claims made about the median of a population.

Recommended Assignment: Exercises 1-10, 13-16

13-3 Wilcoxon Signed-Ranks Test for Matched Pairs

This procedure requires that you sort data, then assign ranks. When working with larger data sets, sorting and ranking is tedious, but software or a TI-83/84 Plus calculator can be used to automate that process. Stem-and-leaf plots can also be very helpful in sorting data.

Because the methods of this section and the following section both involve names of "Wilcoxon," it is easy to confuse the two methods or to forget which method is appropriate for independent samples and which is appropriate for matched pairs. The textbook suggests that confusion can be avoided by using the Internal Revenue Service for the mnemonic of IRS to remind us of "independent: rank sum". That is, if the samples are independent, use the rank sum test. But the methods of this section involve matched pairs (instead of independent samples), use the signed-ranks test.

Activity: Use the same activity suggested for Section 13-3.

Extra Example: In low-speed crash tests of five BMW cars, the repair costs were computed for a factory-authorized repair center and an independent repair facility. The results are listed in the accompanying table. Use the sign test with a 0.05 significance level to test the claim that the paired values have differences with a median equal to 0.

Authorized repair center	\$797	\$571	\$904	\$1147	\$418	\$1442
Independent repair center	\$523	\$488	\$875	\$911	\$297	\$898

(Answer: Test statistic is $T = 0$. Critical value is 1. Reject the null hypothesis that the median of the differences is equal to 0. There appears to be a significant difference between the costs from the two repair facilities.)

Minimum Outcome Objectives After completing Section 13-3, students should be able to apply the Wilcoxon signed-ranks test for sample data consisting of matched pairs.

Recommended Assignment: Exercises 1-8

13-4 Wilcoxon Rank-Sum Test for Two Independent Samples

The test described in this section is equivalent to the Mann-Whitney *U* test described in some other textbooks. Also, some technologies have a feature for the Mann-Whitney *U* test, so those features can be used for this section.

Activity: (This is the same activity suggested for Section 9-3.) Use the measured pulse rates from the class to test for a difference between the mean pulse rate of men and the mean pulse rate of women.

Extra Example: Listed below are weights (grams) of randomly selected M&M plain candies. Use a 0.05 significance level to test the claim that yellow M&Ms and brown M&Ms have the same median.

Yellow:	0.883	0.769	0.859	0.784	0.824	0.858	0.848	0.851
Brown:	0.696	0.876	0.855	0.806	0.840	0.868	0.859	0.982

(Answer: The first rank sum is 61.5, $\mu = 68$, $\sigma = 9.5219$. Test statistic is $z = -0.68$. Critical values are $z = -1.96$ and 1.96. *P*-value = 0.4949. Fail to reject the null hypothesis of equal medians. Yellow M&Ms and brown M&Ms appear to have weights with the same median.)

Minimum Outcome Objectives After completing Section 13-4, students should be able to apply the Wilcoxon rank-sum test for sample data from two independent populations.

Recommended Assignment: Exercises 1-8

13-5 Kruskal-Wallis Test

This section deals with comparisons of three or more sets of sample data, so it could be covered along with Section 12-2 (ANOVA). The advantage of the Kruskal–Wallis test is that unlike the ANOVA methods of Section 12–2, there is no requirement that the populations have a normal distribution or any other particular distribution. If the class lacks sufficient time or energy to study analysis of variance, this section might be used as a quicker and easier alternative.

Extra Example: The accompanying table lists the body temperatures of five randomly selected subjects from each of three different age groups. Use a 0.05 significance level to test the claim that the three age-group populations have the same median body temperature.

Body Temperatures (ºF) Categorized by Age

18–20	21–29	30 and older
98.0	99.6	98.6
98.4	98.2	98.6
97.7	99.0	97.0
98.5	98.2	97.5
97.1	97.9	97.3

(Answer: The rank sums are 35, 52, 33. Test statistic is $H = 2.1800$. Critical value is 5.991. P-value = 0.3362. There is not sufficient evidence to warrant rejection of the claim that the three age-group populations have the same median body temperature.)

Activity: (This is essentially the same activity suggested for Section 12-3.) First, partition the students into three or four groups according to major or type of major (such as liberal arts, math or science, history or economics, and "other"). Then ask each student to estimate the length of the classroom. Collect the estimates and group them according to the different categories, then test the claim that the different groups will produce estimates with the same median.

Minimum Outcome Objectives After completing Section 13-5, students should be able to apply the Kruskal-Wallis test for sample data from three or more independent populations.

Recommended Assignment: Exercises 1-5, 8, 10

13-6 Rank Correlation

Recommendation: Cover this section along with Section 10–2. Section 10–2 has a requirement of a normal distribution, but this section does not require a normal distribution or any other particular distribution.

Activity: (This is the same activity suggested for Section 10–2.) Consider doing an in-class example with six pairs of data. Randomly select six students and use their pulse rates and heights. Test for a correlation between those two variables.

Extra Example: Many of us have heard that the tip should be 15% of the bill. The accompanying table lists some sample data collected from the author's students. Use the sample data and use the rank correlation coefficient to determine whether there is sufficient evidence to conclude that there is a relationship between the amount of the bill and the amount of the tip.

Bill ($)	33.46	50.68	87.92	98.84	63.60	107.34
Tip ($)	5.50	5.00	8.08	17.00	12.00	16.00

(Answer: Test statistic is $r_s = 0.829$. Critical values are -0.886 and 0.886, assuming a 0.05 significance level. Fail to reject the null hypothesis of no correlation. There does not appear to be correlation between the amount of the bill and the amount of the tip.)

Minimum Outcome Objectives After completing Section 13-6, students should be able to compute the value of the rank correlation coefficient r_s, and use it to determine whether there is a correlation between two variables.

Recommended Assignment: Exercises 1–7, 10, 13, 15

13-7 Runs Test for Randomness

Really stress that the runs test for randomness is based on the *order* in which sample data occur. This is *not* a test to determine whether there is a *biased* sample with one group occurring disproportionately more often. The issue of bias could be addressed with other methods, such as the sign test or a parametric test based on proportions (as in Section 8-3 or 9-2).

Activity: Using the seating arrangement of the class, conduct a runs test for randomness in the way that males and females are seated.

Extra Example: A statistics professor observes that students enter her class in groups that appear to consist of mutual friends. She claims that the genders of students who enter her class are not in random order. Use the sample data below to test that claim.

F F F F F F M M F F F F F M M M M M M M M F F F F

(Answer: $n_1 = 15$, $n_2 = 10$, and there are 5 runs. Test statistic is $G = 5$. Critical values are 7 and 18. Reject the null hypothesis of randomness. There is sufficient evidence to support the claim that the order of the genders is not random.)

Minimum Outcome Objectives After completing Section 13-7, students should be able to use the runs test for randomness to determine whether sample data occur in a random sequence.

Recommended Assignment: Exercises 1–8, 10, 11, 14

Chapter 14

This chapter is particularly important for students majoring in business or technology. Due to time constraints, not too many professors are able to include this chapter in their syllabus, and it can be easily omitted.

The decision to include this section might be affected somewhat by the technology that is being used in the course. Minitab is ideal, because it is capable of automatically generating the graphs described in this chapter. Excel can also be used, but use of the DDXL add-in is recommended. If using a technology other than Minitab or Excel, you can cover this chapter by simply using the displays that are available in the textbook.

14-2 Control Charts for Variation and Mean

This section considers the following graphs.

1. Run charts
2. Control charts to monitor the variation in a process
3. Control charts to monitor a process mean.

Section 14-3 considers control charts for monitoring some qualitative attribute, such as the rate of defective items.

Be sure to emphasize and clarify the fact that the control charts are based on *actual* behavior, not *desired* behavior. It is possible to have a manufacturing process in statistical control, but if that process is consistently filling 12 oz cans with only 4 oz of cola, then the process *specifications* are not being met.

Extra Example: The Battlecreek Battery Company manufactures 9 volt batteries. A battery is selected from the production run every 12 minutes, so there is a sample of 5 batteries each hour. The selected batteries are tested for their voltage levels. The $\overline{x}$ chart for 20 consecutive hours of production is given below. Examine that control chart and determine whether the process is within statistical control. (Answer: Production is out of control, because there is a point that lies below the lower control limit.)

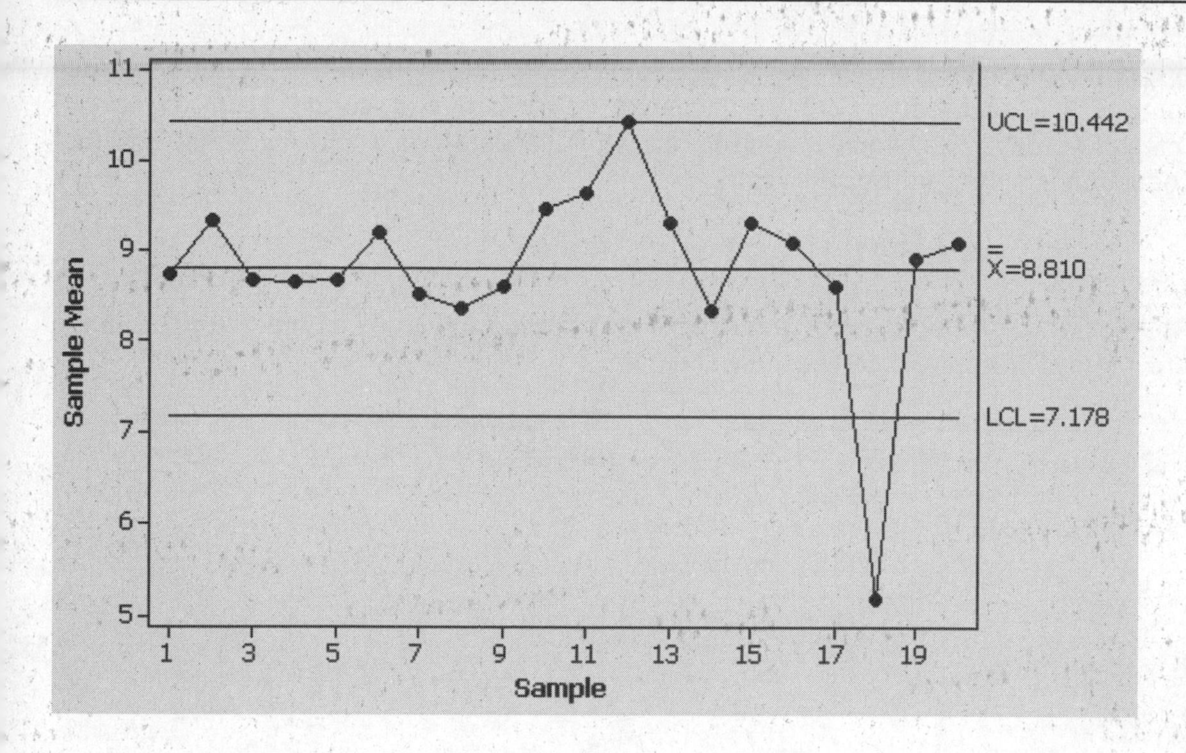

Minimum Outcome Objectives After completing Section 14-2, students should be able to construct a run chart, a control chart for *R*, and a control chart for $\overline{x}$. They should be able to identify out-of-control criteria and apply them to determine whether process data are within statistical control.

Recommended Assignment: Exercises 1-10

14-3 Control Charts for Attributes

Point out that the examples and exercises in Section 14-3 assume that all samples have the same size *n*. There are ways to deal with unequal sample sizes, but we do not consider them in the textbook. (Minitab includes a procedure for automatically making adjustments for different sample sizes. See the *Minitab Manual.*)

Also point out that the upper and lower control limits are essentially the same as confidence interval limits first presented in Section 7-2. 95% confidence interval limits would use 1.96 instead of 3. The use of "3" corresponds to a confidence level of 99.7%.

Activity: If this topic is included, it is probably covered closer to the end of the course, so there should be a record of attendance up to this point. Assume that the class size is constant and list the numbers of absences up to this point. Use a control chart to determine whether absences are in statistical control.

Extra Example: The Mighty Mouse Manufacturing Company manufactures 500 computer mice each day. (As of this writing, it has not been established that "mice" is the correct plural of a computer mouse, but "mice" seems to be much more common than "mouses.") Listed below are the numbers of defective mice on each of several consecutive days. Construct a control chart for the defect rate and determine whether production is within statistical control.

8 7 8 8 6 9 8 12 11 9 14 11 11 18 19

(Answer: The process is out of statistical control because there is an upward trend in the defect rate. The control chart is shown below.)

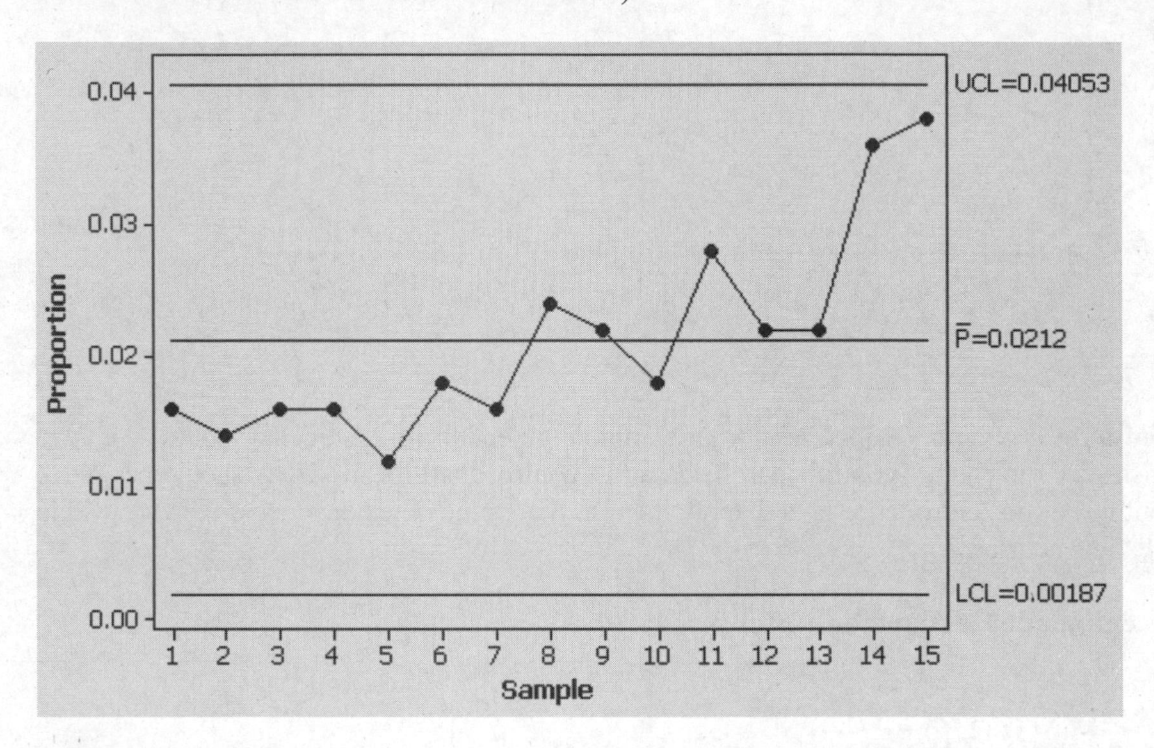

Minimum Outcome Objectives After completing Section 14-3, students should be able to construct a control chart for *p*. They should be able to identify out-of-control criteria and apply them to determine whether process attribute data are within statistical control.

Recommended Assignment: Exercises 1-9, 12

Chapter 15

Section 15-1 discusses a final project. Inclusion of such a project is one way to dramatically increase the effectiveness of the introductory statistics course. Such a final project can be an *extremely* worthwhile and valuable experience for students, and such a project should be included if at all possible. Here are some suggestions for a successful final project:

- Require that topics be approved, and carefully scrutinize topics for anything that might cause problems, such as surveys of sexual behavior, inappropriate measurements of people, topics that would involve invasions of privacy, and so on.

- Emphasize that the project involves cooperation within a group, computer usage, preparation of a report, and an oral presentation. All of these requirements involve important job skills that employers consider extremely valuable.

- Select groups of three or four students each. Try to select one student from each quartile (based on grades).

- Avoid having close friends in the same group. Try to achieve a good mixture of cultures, ages, genders, and personality types.

- For evaluation, ask that each student write a sentence describing the level of involvement of each of the other group members.

- Deadline: An absolute deadline should be the fourth class before the end. This will allow for more than a full class of group presentations and at least a class or two devoted to review for a final exam.

IV. Selecting a Technology

Here are the technologies used in introductory statistics courses:

- **STATDISK**
- **Minitab**
- **Excel**
- **TI-83 Plus or TI-84 Plus calculator**
- **Any scientific calculator**
- **SPSS**
- **SAS**
- **Other: Fathom, JMP, Statistica, R, Stata, . . .**

There is no technology that is universally best for all statistics courses. The technology that is selected should reflect the needs and facilities of individual colleges.

Recommendations for Using Technology

Again, keep in mind that these recommendations are from the author, they are not given in an authoritarian spirit of "you must do it this way," and you should carefully consider the special needs of your students.

The author recommends that instead of allowing students to use "any" scientific calculator, the class should use a specific statistical software package or a TI-83 Plus or TI-84 Plus calculator. If a TI-83 Plus or TI-84 Plus calculator is required, the author recommends that students do at least a few simple projects using statistical software. The author's personal preference is to require that each student have either a TI-83 Plus calculator or a TI-84 Plus calculator, along with STATDISK used for several different projects. However, the author's personal preferences are not universally suitable for all colleges. See comments about individual technologies below.

The author recommends that instead of using the tables in Appendix A from the textbook, students use the statistical software package or TI-83/84 Plus calculator to find critical values and/or *P*-values. The author recommends that the *P*-value method of testing hypotheses be emphasized (although there is some value in learning the traditional method as well).

The author recommends that technology be used not only for routine statistical functions, but also for other methods made available by technology, such as simulations. For example, use simulations as a way to conduct a few hypothesis tests, so that students can see hypothesis testing from a different perspective. Technology can help you circumvent number-crunching and working with formulas, so that students can better focus on important concepts.

STATDISK STATDISK is a free statistical software package that is on the CD included with the textbook. It is free to colleges that adopt the textbook. Updates can be found on the Web site www.aw-bc.com/triola. It is very easy to run, and it can be used with almost every major procedure in the textbook. The data sets from Appendix B in the textbook are already stored in STATDISK, so they can be easily accessed.

Advantages of using STATDISK:

1. It is free. (It is on the CD included with new copies of the textbook.)
2. It is easy to use.
3. It can be used for almost every major procedure in the textbook.
4. Because it is designed specifically for the textbook, it is consistent with the procedures in the textbook.

Helpful supplements for STATDISK users:

1. *STATDISK Student Laboratory Manual and Workbook*
2. Updates at the Web site www.aw-bc.com/triola

Minitab Minitab is a rich and powerful statistical software package that is used by many colleges and businesses. It was once expensive, but there are now inexpensive options available for students. Minitab was once limited in the sense that it required lists of the original sample values, but it now allows the use of summary statistics. Minitab is particularly attractive if the statistics classes are held in a computer lab, with each student having immediate access to Minitab.

Advantages of using Minitab:

1. It can be inexpensive. Students can rent Minitab for a semester at a cost of about $26. Minitab can cost as little as $10 when the Student Version of Minitab is bundled with the textbook.
2. Minitab is a professional and commercial statistical software package, and it has an extensive list of functions.

Helpful supplements for Minitab users:

1. The Appendix B data sets are available as Minitab worksheets on the CD that is included with the textbook.
2. *Minitab Manual*, which is a printed supplement to the textbook

Excel Excel is a spreadsheet program used extensively by businesses and other organizations. Many statistics professors choose Excel because they believe that they are helping their students to learn technical skills that will be very helpful when they enter the working world. Because Excel is included as part of many Microsoft packages, it is essentially free for many students. *Caution*: Excel is known to have some statistical shortcomings, so be sure to use some type of guide so that you know when Excel itself can be used and when an “add-in” (supplement) must be used instead. The Triola statistics textbook series includes an Excel version: *Elementary Statistics Using Excel*.

Advantages of using Excel:

1. It is essentially free for many students.
2. Students learn Excel, which will likely help them in their future employment.

Helpful supplements for Excel users:

1. DDXL (an Excel add-in that is on the CD included with the textbook), which is a supplement that can be installed in Excel. DDXL adds important statistical functions, and it correctly handles some cases that Excel does not.
2. The Appendix B data sets are available in an Excel format on the CD that is included with the textbook.
3. *Excel Student Laboratory and Manual*, which is a separate printed supplement to the textbook.

TI-83 Plus or TI-84 Plus Calculator Either calculator (TI-83 Plus or TI-84 Plus) can be used. As of this writing, TI-83 Plus calculators are less expensive, selling for around $80. When the author first required the TI calculator, he had serious concerns about requiring an expensive item in addition to the textbook. He therefore announced that students could sell back their calculators at the end of the semester for half of its cost, and those calculators could then be sold to next semester's statistics students. The author was astounded to see that *no* students wanted to sell their calculators at the end of the semester. This was a strong indication that students saw real value in the calculators, and the cost was not a serious factor once they saw their value. Some colleges have rental programs designed to keep calculator costs low. Some colleges have a program for providing free calculators to students who cannot afford them.

Advantages of requiring a TI-83/84 Plus calculator:

1. Every student has the calculator in class, so the calculator can be used in class and on tests.
2. The calculator has an extensive list of statistical functions, so it is quite powerful.
3. The calculator allows analysis of either summary data or original lists of sample data.

Helpful supplements for the TI-83/84 calculator:

1. The CD provided with the textbook includes a TRIOLAXE App (application), which can be download to the calculator, so that students have the data sets from Appendix B in the textbook. This allows for more realistic class examples and test questions, because students can work with large data sets without manually keying in long lists of data.
2. The CD provided with the textbook includes programs that can be downloaded to the calculator, so more statistical functions can be executed.
3. *Graphing Calculator Manual for the TI-83 Plus, TI-84 Plus, and the TI-89*, which is a separate printed supplement to the textbook.

Recommendations for calculator usage:

1. Instead of using the calculator as the only technology, also require that a few simple projects be completed by using a statistical software package on a computer.

2. Run the CtlgHelp application so that the syntax of functions can be seen and there is no need to memorize that syntax. To run the CtlgHelp application, press the **APPS** key, select **CtlgHelp**, then press the **ENTER** key.

For example, select the **DISTR** menu (by pressing **2nd**, then pressing the **VARS** key), scroll to **binompdf** and press the + key before pressing **ENTER**. The screen display will show that the syntax of the binompdf function is (numtrials, p[,x]). That is, you must enter the number of trials followed by a comma followed by a probability value. The entry of a specific number of successes x is optional (as indicated by the brackets). The command binompdf(50, .4, 23) yields the binomial probability of getting 23 successes in 50 trials when the probability of success is 0.4. Students need not memorize the syntax of functions, because it is readily available.

SPSS SPSS has a relatively inexpensive student version available. SPSS typically requires original lists of sample values, so summary statistics cannot be used. SPSS is generally more difficult than the preceding technologies.

Advantages of requiring SPSS calculator:

1. SPSS is widely used in social sciences, so some students may encounter it in their future coursework and careers.

Helpful supplements for SPSS users:

1. The Appendix B data sets are available in an SPSS format on the CD that is included with the textbook.
3. *SPSS Student Laboratory and Manual*, which is a separate printed supplement to the textbook.

SAS SAS has a relatively inexpensive student version available but, as of this writing, it is impractical because it allows only 49 data values.

Helpful supplements for SAS users:

1. The Appendix B data sets are available in an SAS format on the CD that is included with the textbook.
3. *SAS Student Laboratory and Manual*, which is a separate printed supplement to the textbook.

V. General Teaching Tips

I. How to Be an Effective Teacher

(From David Royse, *Teaching Tips for College and University Instructors: A Practical Guide*, published by Allyn & Bacon, Boston, MA. © 2001 by Pearson Education, Inc. Adapted by permission of the publisher.)

A look at fifty years of research "on the way teachers teach and learners learn" reveals five broad principles of good teaching practice (Chickering and Gamson, 1987).

Five Principles of Good Teaching Practice

1. **Frequent student-faculty contact:** Faculty who are concerned about their students and their progress and who are perceived to be easy to talk to, serve to motivate and keep students involved.

   Things you can do to apply this principle:
   • Attend events sponsored by students.
   • Serve as a mentor or advisor to students.
   • Keep "open" or "drop-in" office hours.

2. **The encouragement of cooperation among students:** There is a wealth of research indicating that students benefit from the use of small-group and peer-learning instructional approaches.

   Things you can do to apply this principle:
   • Have students share in class their interests and backgrounds.
   • Create small groups to work on projects together.
   • Encourage students to study together.

3. **Prompt feedback:** Learning theory research has consistently shown that the quicker the feedback, the greater the learning.

   Things you can do to apply this principle:
   • Return quizzes and exams by the next class meeting.
   • Return homework within one week.
   • Provide students with detailed comments on their written papers.

4. **Emphasize time on task:** This principle refers to the amount of actual involvement with the material being studied and applied, obviously, to the way the instructor uses classroom instructional time. Faculty need good time-management skills.

   Things you can do to apply this principle:
   • Require students who miss class to make up lost work.
   • Require students to rehearse before making oral presentations.
   • Don't let class breaks stretch out too long.

5. **Communicating high expectations:** The key here is not to make the course impossibly difficult but to have goals that can be attained as long as individual learners stretch and work hard, going beyond what they already know.

Things you can do to apply this principle:
- Communicate expectations orally and in writing at the beginning of the course.
- Explain the penalties for students who turn work in late.
- Identify excellent work by students; display exemplars if possible.

↔Tips for Thriving:
Creating an Inclusive Classroom
How do you model an open, accepting attitude within your classroom where students will feel it is safe to engage in give-and-take discussions? First, view students as individuals instead of representatives of separate and distinct groups. Cultivate a climate that is respectful of diverse viewpoints, and don't allow ridicule, or defamatory or hurtful remarks. Try to encourage everyone in the class to participate, and be alert to showing favoritism.

II. Planning Your Course

(From David Royse, *Teaching Tips for College and University Instructor's: A Practical Guide,* published by Allyn & Bacon, Boston, MA. © 2001 by Pearson Education, Inc. Adapted by permission of the publisher.)

Constructing the syllabus: The syllabus should clearly communicate course objectives, assignments, required readings, and grading policies. Think of the syllabus as a stand-alone document. Those students who miss the first or second meeting of a class should be able to learn most of what they need to know about the requirements of the course from reading the syllabus. Start by collecting syllabi from colleagues who have recently taught the course you will be teaching and look for common threads and themes.

Problems to avoid: One mistake commonly made by educators teaching a course for the first time is that they may have rich and intricate visions of how they want students to demonstrate comprehension and synthesis of the material, but they somehow fail to convey this information to those enrolled. Check your syllabus to make sure your expectations have been fully articulated. Be very specific. Avoid vaguely worded instructions that can be misinterpreted.

↔Tips for Thriving:
Visual Quality
Students today are highly visual learners, so you should give special emphasis to the visual quality of the materials you provide to students. Incorporate graphics into your syllabus and other handouts. Color-code your materials so material for different sections of the course are on different colored papers. Such visuals are likely to create a perception among students that you are contemporary.

III. Your First Class

(From Richard E. Lyons, Marcella L. Kysilka, & George E. Pawlas, *The Adjunct Professor's Guide to Success: Surviving and Thriving In The Classroom,* published by Allyn & Bacon, Boston, MA. © 1999 by Pearson Education, Inc. Adapted by permission of the publisher.)

Success in achieving a great start is almost always directly attributable to the quality and quantity of planning that has been invested by the course professor. If the first meeting of your class is to be successful, you should strive to achieve seven distinct goals.

Seven Goals for a Successful First Meeting

1. **Create a positive first impression:** Renowned communications consultant Roger Ailes claims you have fewer than 10 seconds to create a positive image of yourself. Students are greatly influenced by the visual component; therefore, you must look the part of the professional professor. Dress as you would for a professional job interview. Greet each student entering the room. Be approachable and genuine.

2. **Introduce yourself effectively:** Communicate to students who you are and why you are credible as the teacher of the course. Seek to establish your approachability by "building common ground," such as stating your understanding of students' hectic lifestyles or their common preconceptions toward the subject matter.

3. **Clarify the goals and expectations:** Make a transparency (or PowerPoint display) of each page of the syllabus for display on a projector and using a cover sheet, expose each section as you explain it. Provide clarification and elicit questions.

4. **Conduct an activity that introduces students to each other:** Students' chances of being able to complete a course effectively is enhanced if each comes to perceive the classmates as a "support network." The small amount of time you invest in an icebreaker will help create a positive classroom atmosphere and pay additional dividends throughout the term.

5. **Learn students' names:** A student who is regularly addressed by name feels more valued, is invested more effectively in classroom discussion, and will approach the professor with questions and concerns.

6. **Whet students' appetite for the course material:** The textbook adopted for the course is critical to your success. Your first meeting should include a review of its approach, features, and sequencing. Explain to students what percentage of class tests will be derived from material from the textbook.

7. **Reassure students of the value of the course:** At the close of your first meeting reassure students that the course will be a valuable learning experience and a wise investment of their time. Review the reasons why the course is a good investment: important and relevant content, interesting classmates, and a dynamic classroom environment.

IV. Strategies for Teaching and Learning

(From David Royse, *Teaching Tips for College and University Instructors: A Practical Guide,* published by Allyn & Bacon, Boston, MA. © 2001 by Pearson Education. Inc. Adapted by permission of the publisher.)

Team learning: The essential features of this small group learning approach, developed originally for use in large college classrooms are (1) relatively permanent heterogeneous task groups; (2) grading based on a combination of individual performance, group performance, and peer evaluation; (3) organization of the course so that the majority of class time is spent on small group activities; (4) a six-step instructional process similar to the following model:

1. Individual study of material outside of the class is assigned.
2. Individual testing is used (multiple-choice questions over homework at the beginning of class).
3. Groups discuss their answers and then are given a group test of the same items. They then get immediate feedback (answers).
4. Groups may prepare written appeals of items.
5. Feedback is given from instructor.
6. An application-oriented activity is assigned (e.g., a problem to be solved requiring input from all group members).

If you plan to use team learning in your class, inform students at the beginning of the course of your intentions to do so and explain the benefits of small group learning. Foster group cohesion by sitting groups together and letting them choose "identities" such as a team name or slogan. You will need to structure and supervise the groups and ensure that the projects build on newly acquired learning. Make the projects realistic and interesting and ensure that they are adequately structured so that each member's contribution is 25 percent. Students should be given criteria by which they can assess and evaluate the contributions of their peers on a project-by-project basis (Michaelsen, 1994).

↔Tips for Thriving:
Active Learning and Lecturing
Lecturing is one of the most time-honored teaching methods, but does it have a place in an active learning environment? There are times when lecturing can be effective. Think about the following when planning a lecture:

Build interest: Capture your students' attention by leading off with an anecdote or cartoon.
Maximize understanding and retention: Use brief handouts and demonstrations as a visual backup to enable your students to see as well as hear.
Involve students during the lecture: Interrupt the lecture occasionally to challenge students to answer spot quiz questions.
Reinforce the lecture: Give students a self-scoring review test at the end of the lecture.

V. Grading and Assessment Techniques

(From Philip C. Wankat, *The Effective, Efficient Professor: Teaching Scholarship And Service,* published by Allyn & Bacon, Boston, M. © 2002 by Pearson Education, Inc. Adapted by permission of the publisher.)

Philosophy of grading: Develop your own philosophy of grading by picturing in your mind the performance of typical A students, B students and so on. Try different grading methods until you find one that fits your philosophy and is reasonably fair. Always look closely at students on grade borders—take into account personal factors if the group is small. Be consistent with or slightly more generous than the procedure outlined in your syllabus.

Criterion grading: Professor Philip Wankat writes: "I currently use a form of criterion grading for my sophomore and junior courses. I list the scores in the syllabus that will guarantee the students A's, B's, and so forth. For example, a score of 85 to 100 guarantees an A; 75 to 85, a B; 65 to 75, a C; and 55 to 65, a D. If half the class gets above 85% they all get an A. This reduces competition and allows students to work together and help each other. The standard grade gives students something to aim for and tells them exactly what their grade is at any time. For students whose net scores are close to the borders at the end of the course, I look at other factors before deciding a final grade, such as attendance."

↔**Tips for Thriving:**
Result Feedback
As stated earlier, feedback on results is the most effective of motivating factors. Anxious students are especially hungry for positive feedback. You can quickly and easily provide it by simply writing "Great job!" on the answer sheets or tests. For students who didn't perform well, a brief note such as "I'd love to talk with you at the end of class" can be especially reassuring. The key is to be proactive and maintain high standards, while requiring students to retain ownership of their success.

VI. Managing Problem Situations

(From Philip C. Wankat. *The Effective, Efficient Professor: Teaching, Scholarship And Service,* published by Allyn & Bacon, Boston, MA. © 2002 by Pearson Education, Inc. Adapted by permission of the publisher.)

Cheating: Cheating is one behavior that should not be tolerated. Tolerating cheating tends to make it worse. Prevention of cheating is much more effective than trying to cure it once it has occurred. A professor can prevent cheating by:

- Creating rapport with students
- Gaining a reputation for giving fair tests
- Giving clear instructions and guidelines before, during, and after tests
- Educating students on the ethics of plagiarism
- Requiring periodic progress reports and outlines before a paper is due

Try to develop exams that are perceived as fair and secure by students. Often, the accusation that certain questions were tricky is valid as it relates to ambiguous language and trivial material. Ask your mentor or an experienced instructor to closely review the final draft of your first few exams for these factors.

(From David Royse, *Teaching Tips for College and University Instructors: A Practical Guide,* published by Allyn & Bacon, Boston, MA. © 2001 by Pearson Education, Inc. Adapted by permission of the publisher.)

Unmotivated students: There are numerous reasons why students may not be motivated. The "required course" scenario is a likely explanation—although politics in colonial America is your life's work, it is safe to assume that not everyone will share your enthusiasm. There are also personal reasons such as a death of a loved one or depression. Whenever you detect a pattern that you assume to be due to lack of motivation (e.g., missing classes, not handing assignments in on time, nonparticipation in class), arrange a time to have the student meet with you outside the classroom. Candidly express your concerns and then listen.

↔Tips for Thriving:
Discipline
One effective method for dealing with some discipline problems is to ask the class for feedback (Angelo & Cross, 1993). In a one-minute quiz, ask the students, "What can I do to help you learn?" Collate the responses and present them to the class. If behavior such as excessive talking appears in some responses (e.g., "Tell people to shut up") this gives you the backing to ask students to be quiet. Use of properly channeled peer pressure is often effective in controlling undesired behavior.

Motivating students is part of the faculty member's job. To increase motivation, professors should show enthusiasm for the topic, use various media and methods to present material, use humor in the classroom, employ activities that encourage active learning, and give frequent, positive feedback.

(From Sharon Baiocco, Jamie N. De Waters, *Successful College Teaching: Problem Solving Strategies of Distinguished Professors,* published by Allyn & Bacon, Boston, MA. © 1998 by Pearson Education, Inc. Adapted by permission of the publisher.)

Credibility problems: If you are an inexperienced instructor, you may have problems with students not taking you seriously. At the first class meeting, articulate clear rules of classroom decorum and conduct yourself with dignity and respect for students. Try to exude that you are in charge and are the "authority" and avoid trying to pose as the students' friend.

VII. Improving Your Performance

(From Richard E. Lyons, Marcella L. Kysilka & George E. Pawlas, *The Adjunct Professor's Guide to Success: Surviving and Thriving In The Classroom,* published by Allyn & Bacon, Boston, MA. © 1999 by Pearson Education, Inc. Adapted by permission of the publisher.)

Self-evaluation: The instructor who regularly engages in systematic self-evaluation will unquestionably derive greater reward from the formal methods of evaluation commonly employed by colleges and universities. One method for providing structure to an ongoing system of self-evaluation is to keep a journal of reflections on your teaching experiences. Regularly invest 15 or 20 introspective minutes following each class meeting to focus especially on the strategies and events in class that you feel could be improved. Committing your thoughts and emotions enables you to develop more effective habits, build confidence in your teaching performance, and make more effective comparisons later. The following questions will help guide self-assessment:

How do I typically begin a class?
Where/How do I position myself in the class?
How do I move in the classroom?
Where are my eyes usually focused?
Do I facilitate students' visual processing of course material?
Do I change the speed, volume, energy, and tone of my voice?
How do I ask questions of students?
How often, and when, do I smile or laugh in class?
How do I react when students are inattentive?
How do I react when students disagree or challenge what I say?
How do I typically end a class?

↔Tips for Thriving:
Video-Recording Your Class
In recent years, a wide range of professionals have markedly improved their job performance by employing video recorders in their preparation efforts. As an instructor, an effective method might be to ask your mentor or another colleague to tape a 10-to 15-minute mini-lesson, then to debrief it using the assessment questions above. Critiquing a videotaped session provides objectivity and is therefore more likely to effect change. Involving a colleague as an informal coach will enable you to gain from their experience and perspective.

References

Ailes, R. (1996) *You are the message: Getting what you want by being who you are.* New York: Doubleday.

Chickering, A. W., & Gamson, Z. F. (1987) "Seven principles for good practice in undergraduate education." *AAHE Bulletin,* 39, *3-7.*

Michaelson, L. K. (1994). Team Learning: Making a case for the small-group option. In K. W. Prichard & R. M. Sawyer (Eds.), *Handbook of college teaching.* Westport, CT: Greenwood Press.

Sorcinelli, M. D. (1991). Research findings on the seven principles. In A.W. Chickering & Z. Gamson (eds.). "Applying the seven principles of good practice in undergraduate education." *New Directions for Teaching and Learning*. San Francisco: Jossey-Bass.

VI. Top 20 Topics

When planning a course syllabus, try not to place a high priority on covering as many topics as possible. Some topics should be omitted to make time for technology, activities, and projects. Here is a list of core topics which, in the author's humble opinion, should be included. Enclosed within parentheses are the locations in *Elementary Statistics*, 10th edition, where the topics are discussed. These *Top 20 Topics* are identified by a special icon in *Elementary Statistics*, 10th edition.

1. Design of experiments (Section 1-4)
2. Sampling (Section 1-4)
3. Histogram for visualizing distribution (Section 2-2)
4. Measures of center (Section 3-2)
5. Measures of variation (Section 3-3)
6. Outliers (Sections 2-1 and 3-5)
7. Probability: Basic definitions (Section 4-2)
8. Random variables (Section 5-2)
9. Binomial probabilities (Section 5-3)
10. Normal distribution: Finding probabilities and values (Sect. 6-2 and 6-3)
11. Sampling distributions (Section 6-4)
12. Central limit theorem (Section 6-5)
13. Confidence interval for a proportion (Section 7-2)
14. Sample size for estimating a proportion (Section 7-2)
15. Confidence interval for a mean (Section 7-4)
16. Hypothesis test with a proportion (Section 8-3)
17. Hypothesis test with a mean (Section 8-5)
18. Hypothesis test with two proportions (Section 9-2)
19. Linear correlation (Section 10-2)
20. Linear regression (Section 10-3)

VII. Syllabi

The *Annotated Instructor's Edition* of *Elementary Statistics*, 10th edition, includes six different versions of syllabi for the introductory statistics course, and they are reproduced on the following pages. It is important to know that the book contains much more material than can be covered in the typical one-semester introductory statistics course.

When selecting the sections to be included, consider assigning some sections as out-of-class independent work. For example, after students understand the basic concepts of confidence intervals and hypothesis testing, consider assigning exercises from Chapter 9 (Inferences From Two Samples) to be done using a computer software package or a TI-83/84 Plus calculator. This is an excellent way to include important and useful concepts while encouraging students to extend their basic knowledge to different circumstances.

The sample syllabus version B is designed for a more relaxed pace, and it provides for greater opportunities to include technology, activities, and projects.

Note: The "class hour" referred to in the following course outlines consists of approximately one hour.

Syllabus Version A

Class Hour	Text Section	Topic
1	1-1, 1-2, 1-3	Overview; Nature of Data; Critical Thinking
2	1-4	Design of Experiments
3	2-1, 2-2, 2-3	Frequency Distributions and Histograms
4	2-4	Statistical Graphics
5	3-2	Measures of Center
6	3-3	Measures of Variation
7	3-3	Measures of Variation
8	3-4	Measures of Relative Standing
9	3-5	Exploratory Data Analysis
10	Ch. 1, 2, 3	Review
11	Ch. 1, 2, 3	Test 1
12	4-1, 4-2, 4-3	Fundamentals of Probability and Addition Rule
13	4-4	Multiplication Rule: Basics
14	5-1, 5-2	Random Variables
15	5-3	Binomial Probability Distributions
16	5-4	Mean, Variance, and Standard Deviation for the Binomial Distribution
17	Ch. 4, 5	Review
18	Ch. 4, 5	Test 2
19	6-1, 6-2	The Standard Normal Distribution
20	6-3	Applications of Normal Distributions
21	6-4	Sampling Distributions and Estimators
22	6-5	The Central Limit Theorem
23	7-1, 7-2	Estimating a Population Proportion
24	7-3	Estimating a Population Mean: σ Known
25	7-4	Estimating a Population Mean: σ Not Known
26	Ch. 6, 7	Review
27	Ch. 6, 7	Test 3
28	8-1, 8-2	Basics of Hypothesis Testing
29	8-2, 8-3	Testing a Claim about a Proportion
30	8-3	Testing a Claim about a Proportion
31	8-4	Testing a Claim about a Mean: σ Known
32	8-5	Testing a Claim about a Mean: σ Not Known
33	8-6	Testing a Claim about a Standard Deviation or Variance
34	Ch. 8	Review
35	Ch. 8	Test 4
36	10-1, 10-2	Correlation
37	10-2, 10-3	Correlation and Regression
38	10-3	Regression
39	11-3	Contingency Tables
40		Group Project Presentations
41		Group Project Presentations
42	Ch. 10, 11	Review
43	Ch. 10, 11	Test 5
44		Review for Comprehensive Final Exam
45		Review for Comprehensive Final Exam

Syllabus Version B: RELAXED PACE

Class Hour	Text Section	Topic
1	1-1, 1-2	Overview; Nature of Data
2	1-3	Critical Thinking
3	2-1, 2-2, 2-3	Frequency Distributions and Histograms
4	3-2	Measures of Center
5	3-3	Measures of Variation
6	3-3	Measures of Variation
7	3-4	Measures of Relative Standing
8	3-5	Exploratory Data Analysis
9	Ch. 1, 2, 3	Review
10	Ch. 1, 2, 3	Test 1
11	4-1, 4-2	Fundamentals of Probability
12	4-2	Fundamentals of Probability
13	5-1, 5-2	Random Variables
14	5-3	Binomial Probability Distributions
15	5-4	Mean, Variance, and Standard Deviation for the Binomial Distribution
16	Ch. 4, 5	Review
17	Ch. 4, 5	Test 2
18	6-1, 6-2	The Standard Normal Distribution
19	6-3	Applications of Normal Distributions
20	6-3	Applications of Normal Distributions
21	6-5	The Central Limit Theorem
22	7-1, 7-2	Estimating a Population Proportion
23	7-2	Estimating a Population Proportion
24	7-3	Estimating a Population Mean: σ Known
25	7-4	Estimating a Population Mean: σ Not Known
26	Ch. 6, 7	Review
27	Ch. 6, 7	Test 3
28	8-1, 8-2	Basics of Hypothesis Testing
29	8-2, 8-3	Testing a Claim about a Proportion
30	8-3	Testing a Claim about a Proportion
31	8-4	Testing a Claim about a Mean: σ Known
32	8-5	Testing a Claim about a Mean: σ Not Known
33	8-5	Testing a Claim about a Mean: σ Not Known
34	Ch. 8	Review
35	Ch. 8	Test 4
36	10-1, 10-2	Correlation
37	10-2, 10-3	Correlation and Regression
38	10-3	Regression
39		Group Project Presentations
40		Group Project Presentations
41	Ch. 10	Review
42	Ch. 10	Test 5
43		Review for Comprehensive Final Exam
44		Review for Comprehensive Final Exam

Syllabus Version C: EARLY COVERAGE OF CORRELATION AND REGRESSION

Class Hour	Text Section	Topic
1	1-1, 1-2, 1-3	Overview; Nature of Data; Critical Thinking
2	1-4	Design of Experiments
3	2-1, 2-2, 2-3	Frequency Distributions and Histograms
4	3-2	Measures of Center
5	3-3	Measures of Variation
6	3-3	Measures of Variation
7	3-4	Measures of Relative Standing
8	3-5	Exploratory Data Analysis
9	**10-1, 10-2**	**Correlation (Part 1: Basics)**
10	**10-3**	**Regression (Part 1: Basics)**
11	**10–3**	**Regression (Part 1: Basics)**
12	Ch. 1, 2, 3, 10	Review
13	Ch. 1, 2, 3, 10	Test 1
14	4-1, 4-2, 4-3	Fundamentals of Probability and Addition Rule
15	4-4	Multiplication Rule: Basics
16	5-1, 5-2	Random Variables
17	5-3	Binomial Probability Distributions
18	5-4	Mean, Variance, and Standard Deviation for the Binomial Distribution
19	6-1, 6-2	The Standard Normal Distribution
20	6-3	Applications of Normal Distributions
21	6-4	Sampling Distributions and Estimators
22	6-5	The Central Limit Theorem
23	6–6	Normal as Approximation to Binomial
24	Ch. 4, 5, 6	Review
25	Ch. 4, 5, 6	Test 2
26	7-1, 7-2	Estimating a Population Proportion
27	7-3	Estimating a Population Mean: σ Known
28	7-4	Estimating a Population Mean: σ Not Known
29	7-5	Estimating a Population Variance
30	8-1, 8-2	Basics of Hypothesis Testing
31	8-2, 8-3	Testing a Claim about a Proportion
32	8-3	Testing a Claim about a Proportion
33	8-4	Testing a Claim about a Mean: σ Known
34	8-5	Testing a Claim about a Mean: σ Not Known
35	8-6	Testing a Claim about a Standard Deviation or Variance
36	Ch. 7, 8	Review
37	Ch. 7, 8	Test 3
38		Group Project Presentations
39		Group Project Presentations
40		Review for Comprehensive Final Exam
41		Review for Comprehensive Final Exam

Syllabus Version D: MINIMUM COVERAGE OF PROBABILITY

Class Hour	Text Section	Topic
1	1-1, 1-2, 1-3	Overview; Nature of Data; Critical Thinking
2	1-4	Design of Experiments
3	2-1, 2-2, 2-3	Frequency Distributions and Histograms
4	3-2	Measures of Center
5	3-3	Measures of Variation
6	3-3	Measures of Variation
7	3-4	Measures of Relative Standing
8	3-5	Exploratory Data Analysis
9	Ch. 1, 2, 3	Review
10	Ch. 1, 2, 3	Test 1
11	**4-1, 4-2**	**Fundamentals of Probability**
12	5-1, 5-2	Random Variables
13	5-3	Binomial Probability Distributions
14	5-4	Mean, Variance, and Standard Deviation for the Binomial Distribution
15	6-1, 6-2	The Standard Normal Distribution
16	6-3	Applications of Normal Distributions
17	6–4	Sampling Distributions and Estimators
18	6-5	The Central Limit Theorem
19	Ch. 4, 5, 6	Review
20	Ch. 4, 5, 6	Test 2
21	7-1, 7-2	Estimating a Population Proportion
22	7-3	Estimating a Population Mean: σ Known
23	7-4	Estimating a Population Mean: σ Not Known
24	7-5	Estimating a Population Variance
25	8-1, 8-2	Basics of Hypothesis Testing
26	8-2, 8-3	Testing a Claim about a Proportion
27	8-3	Testing a Claim about a Proportion
28	8-4	Testing a Claim about a Mean: σ Known
29	8-5	Testing a Claim about a Mean: σ Not Known
30	8-6	Testing a Claim about Variation
31	Ch. 7, 8	Review
32	Ch. 7, 8	Test 3
33	10-1, 10-2	Correlation
34	10-2, 10-3	Correlation and Regression
35	10-3	Regression
36	11-1, 11-2	Multinomial Experiments
37	11-3	Contingency Tables
38	Ch. 10, 11	Review
39	Ch. 10, 11	Test 4
40		Group Project Presentations
41		Group Project Presentations
42		Review for Comprehensive Final Exam
43		Review for Comprehensive Final Exam

Syllabus Version E: INTEGRATION OF SOME NONPARAMETRIC STATISTICS

Class Hour	Text Section	Topic
1	1-1, 1-2, 1-3	Overview; Nature of Data; Critical Thinking
2	1-4	Design of Experiments
3	13–7	**Runs Test for Randomness**
4	2-1, 2-2, 2-3	Frequency Distributions and Histograms
5	3-2	Measures of Center
6	3-3	Measures of Variation
7	3-3	Measures of Variation
8	3-4	Measures of Position
9	3-5	Exploratory Data Analysis
10	Ch. 1, 2, 3, 13	Review
11	Ch. 1, 2, 3, 13	Test 1
12	4-1, 4-2, 4-3	Fundamentals of Probability and Addition Rule
13	4-4	Multiplication Rule: Basics
14	5-1, 5-2	Random Variables
15	5-3	Binomial Probability Distributions
16	5-4	Mean, Variance, and Standard Deviation for the Binomial Distribution
17	6-1, 6-2	The Standard Normal Distribution
18	6-3	Applications of Normal Distributions
19	6-4	Sampling Distributions and Estimators
20	6-5	The Central Limit Theorem
21	6–6	Normal as Approximation to Binomial
22	Ch. 4, 5, 6	Review
23	Ch. 4, 5, 6	Test 2
24	7-1, 7-2	Estimating a Population Proportion
25	7-3	Estimating a Population Mean: σ Known
26	7-4	Estimating a Population Mean: σ Not Known
27	7-5	Estimating a Population Variance
28	8-1, 8-2	Basics of Hypothesis Testing
29	8-2, 8-3	Testing a Claim about a Proportion
30	8-3	Testing a Claim about a Proportion
31	8-4	Testing a Claim about a Mean: σ Known
32	8-5	Testing a Claim about a Mean: σ Not Known
33	8-6	Testing a Claim about Variation
34	Ch. 7, 8	Review
35	Ch. 7, 8	Test 3
36	10-1, 10-2	Correlation and Regression
37	10-3	Regression
38	**13-6**	**Rank Correlation**
39	**13-3**	**Wilcoxon Signed-Ranks Test**
40	**13-5**	**Kruskal-Wallis Test**
41	Ch. 10, 13	Review
42	Ch. 10, 13	Test 4
43		Group Project Presentations
44		Group Project Presentations
45		Review for Comprehensive Final Exam

Syllabus Version F: Two-Semester Course

A two-semester sequence allows for more time to better incorporate computer usage, cooperative group activities, simulation techniques in probability, and bootstrap resampling techniques in estimating parameters and testing hypotheses.

First Semester:

Chapter 1 (Sections 1-1 through 1-4):	4 classes
Chapter 2 (Sections 2-1 through 2-4):	3 classes
Chapter 3 (Sections 3-1 through 3-5):	5 classes
Chapter 4 (Sections 4-1 through 4-7):	6 classes
Chapter 5 (Sections 5-1 through 5-5):	5 classes
Chapter 6 (Sections 6-1 through 6-7):	6 classes
Chapter 7 (Sections 7-1 through 7-5):	6 classes
Chapter 8 (Sections 8-1 through 8-6):	7 classes

Second Semester:

Chapter 9 (Sections 9-1 through 9-5):	8 classes
Chapter 10 (Sections 10-1 through 10-6):	10 classes
Chapter 11 (Sections 11-1 through 11-4):	5 classes
Chapter 12 (Sections 12-1 through 12-3):	6 classes
Chapter 13 (Sections 13-1 through 13-7):	5 classes
Chapter 14 (Sections 14-1 through 14-3):	6 classes
Chapter 15 (Section 15-1):	3 classes

VIII. Supplements

The student and instructor supplements packages are intended to be the most complete and helpful learning system available for the introductory statistics course. Instructors should contact their local Addison–Wesley sales representative, or e-mail the company directly at exam@aw.com for examination copies.

For the Instructor

- ***Annotated Instructor's Edition,*** by Mario F. Triola, contains answers to all exercises in the margin, plus recommended assignments, and teaching suggestions. ISBN: 0-321-33182-6.
- ***Instructor's Solutions Manual,*** by Milton Loyer (Penn State University), contains solutions to all the exercises and sample course syllabi. ISBN: 0-321-36916-5
- ***Insider's Guide to Teaching with The Triola Statistics Series,*** by Mario F. Triola. You know all about this, because you are reading it now. It contains sample syllabi and tips for incorporating projects, as well as lesson overviews, extra examples, minimum outcome objectives, and recommended assignments for each chapter. ISBN: 0-321-40964-7.
- ***MyStatLab*** (part of the MyMathLab and MathXL product family) is a text-specific, easily customizable online course that integrates interactive multimedia instruction with the textbook content. MyStatLab is powered by CourseCompass™—Pearson Education's online teaching and learning environment—and by MathXL®—our online homework, tutorial, and assessment system. MyStatLab gives you the tools needed to deliver all or a portion of your course online, whether your students are in a lab setting or working from home. MyStatLab provides a rich and flexible set of course materials, featuring free-response tutorial exercises for unlimited practice and mastery. Students can also use online tools, such as video lectures, animations, and a multimedia textbook, to independently improve their understanding and performance. Instructors can use MyStatLab's homework and test managers to select and assign online exercises correlated directly to the textbook, and you can also create and assign your own online exercises and import TestGen tests for added flexibility. MyStatLab's online gradebook—designed specifically for mathematics and statistics—automatically tracks students' homework and test results and gives the instructor control over how to calculate final grades. Instructors can also add offline (paper-and-pencil) grades to the gradebook. MyStatLab is available to qualified adopters. For more information, visit **www.mystatlab.com** or contact your Addison-Wesley sales representative for a demonstration.
- ***Testing System*:** Great care has been taken to create the most comprehensive testing system possible for the new edition of ***Elementary Statistics.*** Not only is there a printed test bank, there is also a computerized test generator, **TestGen,** that allows instructors to view and edit testbank questions, transfer them to tests, and print in a variety of formats. The program also offers many options for sorting, organizing and displaying testbanks and tests. A built-in random number and test generator makes

TestGen ideal for creating multiple versions of tests and provides more possible test items than printed testbank questions. Users can export tests to be compatible with a variety of course management systems, or even just to display in a web browser. Additionally, tests created with TestGen can be used with **QuizMaster**, which enables students to take exams on a computer network. **Printed Testbank** ISBN: 0-321-36914-9; **TestGen** for Mac and Windows ISBN: 0-321-36904-1.

- ***PowerPoint® Lecture Presentation CD*:** Free to qualified adopters, this classroom lecture presentation software is geared specifically to the sequence and philosophy of *Elementary Statistics*. Key graphics from the book are included to help bring the statistical concepts alive in the classroom. These slides are also available on the Triola Web site at **www.aw-bc.com/info/Triola**. Mac and Windows ISBN: 0-321-36905-X.

For the Student

- ***MathXL® for Statistics*** is a powerful online homework, tutorial, and assessment system that accompanies Addison Wesley textbooks in statistics and mathematics. With MathXL for Statistics, instructors can create, edit, and assign online homework created specifically for the Triola textbook and tests using algorithmically generated exercises correlated at the objective level to this book. All student work is tracked in MathXL's online gradebook. Students can take chapter tests in MathXL for Statistics and receive personalized study plans based on their test results. The study plan diagnoses weaknesses and links students directly to tutorial exercises for the objectives they need to study and retest. Students can also access animations and Triola video clips directly from selected exercises. MathXL for Statistics is available to qualified adopters. For more information, visit our website at **www.mathxl.com**, or contact your Addison-Wesley sales representative
- ***Videos*** have been expanded and now supplement most sections in the book, with many topics presented by the author. The videos feature technologies found in the book and the worked-out Chapter Review exercises. This is an excellent resource for students who have missed class or wish to review a topic. It is also an excellent resource for instructors involved with distance learning, individual study, or self-paced learning programs. **Videotape Series** ISBN: 0-321-36913-0. **Digital Video Tutor** (CD–ROM version) ISBN: 0-321-41268-0.
- **Triola *Elementary Statistics* Web Site:** This Web site may be accessed at **http://www.aw-bc.com/triola**, and provides Internet projects keyed to every chapter of the text, plus the book's data sets as they appear on the CD.
- ***Student's Solutions Manual,*** by Milton Loyer (Penn State University), provides detailed, worked-out solutions to all odd-numbered text exercises. ISBN: 0-321-36918-1.

The following technology manuals include instructions on and examples of the technology's use. Each one has been written to correspond with the text.

- ***Excel® Student Laboratory Manual and Workbook,*** written by Johanna Halsey and Ellena Reda (Dutchess Community College), ISBN: 0-321-36909-2.

- ***MINITAB® Manual,*** written by Mario F. Triola. ISBN: 0-321-36919-X.
- ***SAS Student Laboratory Manual and Workbook*** , written by Joseph Morgan ISBN 0-321-36910-6.
- ***SPSS® Student Laboratory Manual and Workbook*** ISBN 0-321-36911-4.
- ***STATDISK Student Laboratory Manual and Workbook,*** written by Mario F. Triola. ISBN: 0-321-36912-2.
- ***Graphing Calculator Manual for the TI-83 Plus, TI-84 Plus, and TI-89,*** by Patricia Humphrey (Georgia Southern University) ISBN: 0-321-36920-3.
- ***ActivStats®***, developed by Paul Velleman and Data Description, Inc., provides complete coverage of introductory statistics topics on CD-ROM, using a full range of multimedia. *ActivStats* integrates video, simulation, animation, narration, text, interactive experiments, World Wide Web access, and Data Desk®, a statistical software package. Homework problems and data sets from the Triola text are included on the CD-ROM. ActivStats for Windows and Macintosh ISBN: 0-321-30364-4. **Also available in versions for Excel, JMP, Minitab, and SPSS**. See your Addison-Wesley sales representative for details or check the Web site at www.aw-bc.com/activstats.
- ***Addison-Wesley Tutor Center:*** Free tutoring is available to students who purchase a new copy of the 10th Edition of *Elementary Statistics* when bundled with an access code. The Addison–Wesley Tutor Center is staffed by qualified statistics and mathematics instructors who provide students with tutoring on text examples and any exercise with an answer in the back of the book. Tutoring assistance is provided by toll-free telephone, fax, e-mail and whiteboard technology—which allows tutors and students to actually see the problems worked while they "talk" in real time over the Internet. This service is available five days a week, seven hours a day. For more information, please contact your Addison–Wesley sales representative.
- ***The Student Edition of MINITAB*** is a condensed version of the professional release of MINITAB Statistical Software. It offers students the full range of MINITAB's statistical methods and graphical capabilities, along with worksheets that can include up to 10,000 data points. It comes with a user's manual that includes case studies and hands-on tutorials, and is perfect for use in any introductory statistics course, including those in the life and social sciences. The currently available Student Edition is The Student Guide to Minitab Release 14. ISBN 0-201-77469-0. MINITAB Student Release 14 statistical software is available for bundling with the Triola textbook. ISBN 0-321-11313-6 (CD only).

Any of these products can be purchased separately, or bundled with Addison–Wesley texts. Instructors can contact local sales representatives for details on purchasing and bundling supplements with the textbook or contact the company at exam@aw.com for examination copies of any of these items.

Getting Started with STATDISK

Overview

STATDISK is a statistics software package this is extremely easy to use, it is free for colleges using a Triola textbook, and it can be used with almost every major statistics method in the textbook.

The Guidelines for Assessment and Instruction in Statistics Education (GAISE) Project was funded by the American Statistical Association, and it includes this recommendation: **"Use technology for developing concepts and analyzing data."** In addition to teaching the content of statistics, we can help our students by strengthening important technology skills. The author's personal recommendation is to select a specific technology instead of having students use a variety of different scientific calculators. The most common choices in introductory statistics courses are Excel, the TI-83/84 Plus calculator, Minitab, or STATDISK.

The author strongly recommends STATDISK as a technology that could be used alone or as a supplement to Excel, the TI-83/84 Plus calculator, Minitab, or any other technology. Please consider taking five minutes to download STATDISK and try it.

Working With STATDISK

1. **Download STATDISK**
   The easiest way to download STATDISK is from the web site, so go to **www.aw.com/triola**, click on the cover of any of the books displayed, then click on the **STATDISK** tab at the left. You can start the download by clicking on the version that you want, such as the STATDISK version for Windows. Save STATDISK in a folder.

2. **Open a Data Set**
   Run STATDISK and select **DATASETS** on the main menu bar, then proceed to select the data set named **Bears**. Note that the bear weights are in column 9.

3. **Explore Data**
   Click on **Data**, select **Explore Data**, select column 9, then click on **Evaluate**. You will see a display that includes descriptive statistics, confidence intervals, a histogram, boxplot, and normal quantile plot. See the following page.

4. **Probability Distributions**
   Ready to throw away your printed tables? Click on **Analysis**, select **Probability Distributions**, then select any of the listed distributions and see how easy it is to get values or areas. For example, try finding the t value corresponding to 73 degrees of freedom and with an area of 0.025 to its right. See the display on the bottom of the following page showing that the t value is 1.992995. **No more problems with limitations of printed tables!!!**

STATDISK Results from Weights of Bears

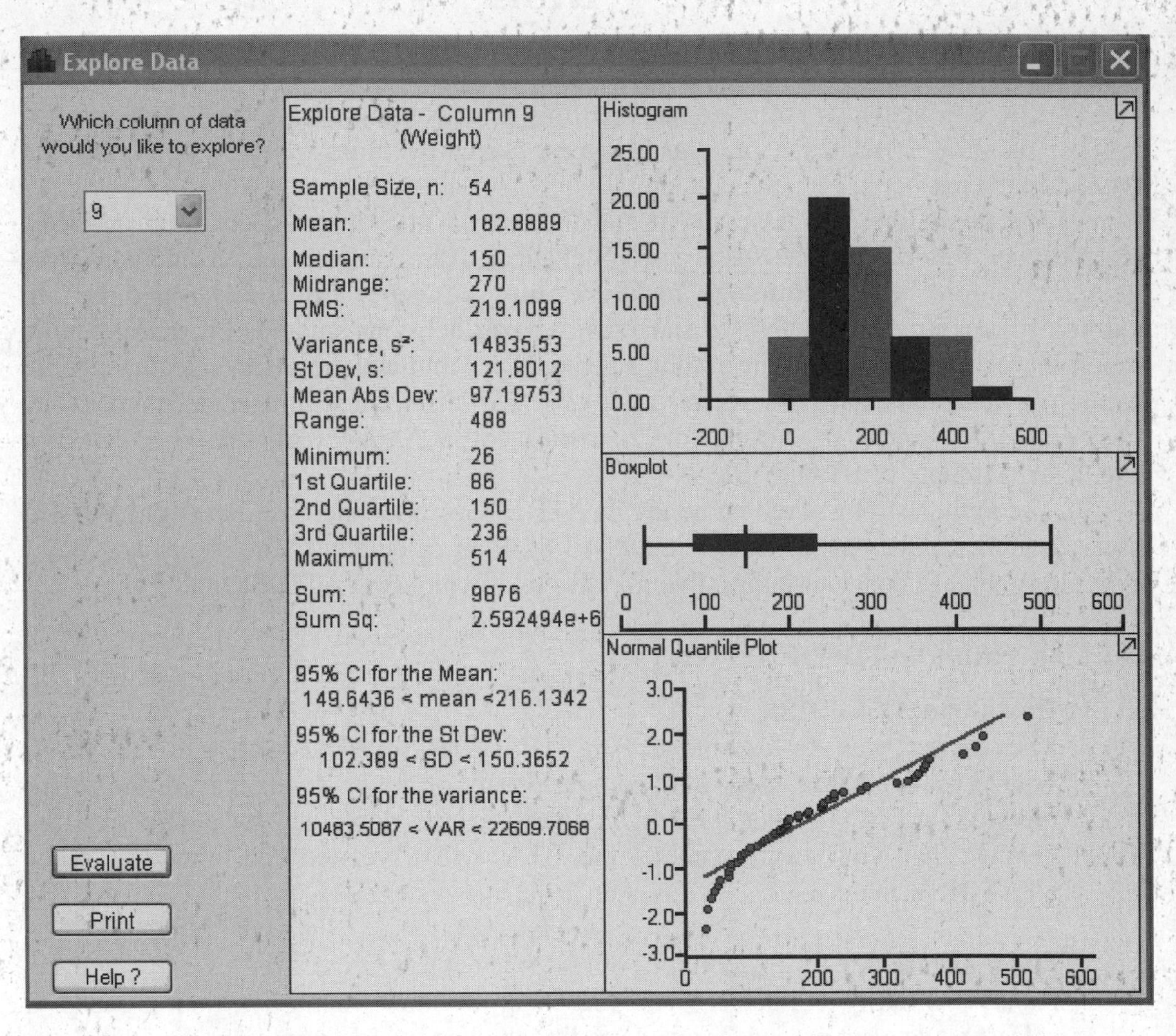

STATDISK: Finding Critical *t* Value

Student t Distribution

Degrees of freedom: 73

Enter one value, then click Evaluate to find the other value.

t Value:

Area to the RIGHT of the t score: 0.025

[Evaluate] [Print]

t Value:	1.992995
Prob Dens:	0.0559822

Cumulative Probs

Left:	0.975000
Right:	0.025000
2 Tailed:	0.050000
Central:	0.950000

73 Degrees Freedom

5. **Hypothesis Test**

Now try a hypothesis test. Click on **Analysis**, select **Hypothesis Testing**, then select the type of test. For example, select **Proportion One Sample** and proceed to use a 0.05 significance level to test the claim that $p = 0.25$ given a sample size of $n = 200$ with 70 successes. Click **Evaluate** to see results. Shown below is the dialog box. You first enter the values at the left, then after clicking **Evaluate,** you get the STATDISK results shown at the right. You could also click on the **Plot** button to get a graph that includes the test statistic and critical values.

STATDISK Hypothesis Test With One Proportion

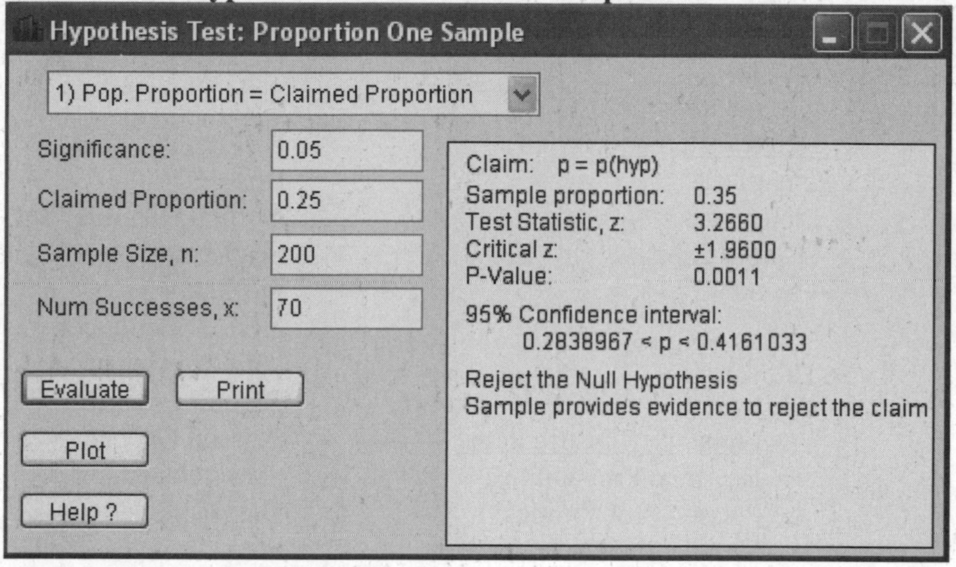

Hypothesis Test: Proportion One Sample

1) Pop. Proportion = Claimed Proportion

Significance: 0.05
Claimed Proportion: 0.25
Sample Size, n: 200
Num Successes, x: 70

Evaluate Print
Plot
Help ?

Claim: p = p(hyp)
Sample proportion: 0.35
Test Statistic, z: 3.2660
Critical z: ±1.9600
P-Value: 0.0011
95% Confidence interval:
0.2838967 < p < 0.4161033
Reject the Null Hypothesis
Sample provides evidence to reject the claim

6. **Other STATDISK Functions**

Click on the main menu items of **Analysis** and **Data** to see other STATDISK functions, including correlation and regression, confidence intervals, contingency tables, analysis of variance, and many other functions. *See the menu configuration on the following page.*

Hint About Using Technology

STATDISK requires little or no classroom time for instruction, but other technologies do require some time. Instructors typically find that time is at a premium, especially if they are using technology and including projects. Consider using technology to *save* some time. For example, after covering confidence intervals and hypothesis testing for situations with *one* population, assign some exercises involving *two* populations and allow students to solve the exercises by using technology. Save valuable class time while encouraging students to expand the scope of what they were taught in earlier chapters.

The author is very proud of the ease and quality of STATDISK, especially because it has been completely reprogrammed by his son, Marc Triola. After seeing how easy and effective STATDISK is, you can proceed to improve the use of technology in your course by including STATDISK. The author thanks all of those statistics teachers who have made suggestions in the past, and we welcome any new suggestions for improving STATDISK.

STATDISK's Menu Configuration

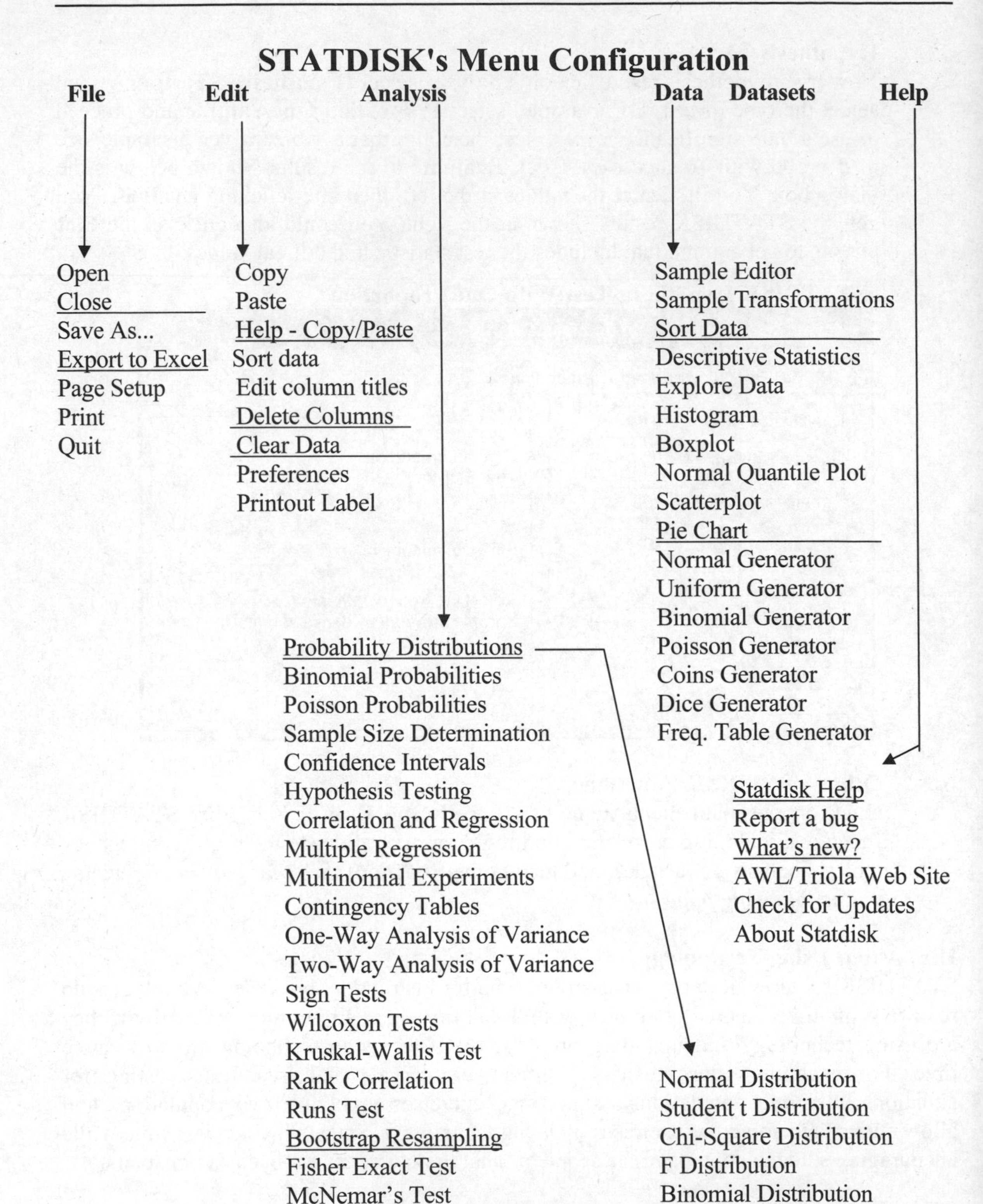

Getting Started with MyStatLab™

Overview

Powered by CourseCompass™ and MathXL®, MyStatLab is a series of text-specific online courses that accompany Pearson Addison-Wesley and Pearson Prentice Hall textbooks in Mathematics and Statistics. Since 2001, more than one million students at over 1100 colleges and universities have had more success in Math with MyStatLab's dependable and easy-to-use online homework, guided solutions, multimedia, tests, and eBooks. Pearson's premier, proven service teams provide training and support when you need it. And MyStatLab offers the broadest range of titles available for adoption.

When you adopt the MyStatLab course for your textbook, your students can view the textbook pages in electronic form and link to supplemental multimedia resources—such as animations and video clips—directly from the eBook. MyStatLab provides students with algorithmically-generated tutorial exercises correlated to the exercises in their text, and the system generates individualized study plans based on student test results. MyStatLab's powerful homework and test managers and flexible online gradebook make it easy for instructors to create and manage online assignments that are automatically graded, so they can spend less time grading and more time teaching!

How to Adopt MyStatLab

1. **Getting Access**
   If you are interested in using MyStatLab for one or more of your courses, you will need an **instructor access code**. You can receive an instructor access code in one of two ways:
   - Request a *MyStatLab Instructor Access Kit* from your Addison-Wesley sales representative. To identify your sales representative, go to **www.aw-bc.com/replocator.**
   - Request an access code online by visiting the **Getting Started** section of the MyStatLab website at **www.mystatlab.com**.

2. **Registering**
   MyStatLab courses are accessed through an online learning environment called CourseCompass, so to adopt a MyStatLab course, you need to register in CourseCompass. Registering is an easy process that takes only a few minutes, and you need to register only once, even if you are teaching more than one MyStatLab course. As part of the registration process, you select a login name and password that you will use from then on to access your MyStatLab course. Once you have your instructor access code, go to **www.coursecompass.com**, click the **Register** button for instructors, and follow the on-screen instructions to register and log in.

3. **Creating Your MyStatLab Course**
   Once you've registered in CourseCompass, creating your MyStatLab course is easy! You will simply be asked to select the course materials for your textbook and enter some very basic information about your course. Approximately one business day later (and often after only an hour or two), you will be notified via e-mail that your course is ready, and you will then be able to log in and begin exploring MyStatLab.

4. **Ordering Books for Your Students**
   To access your MyStatLab course, each student needs to register in CourseCompass using a student access code. The easiest way to supply your students with access codes is to order your textbook packaged with the *MyStatLab Student Access Kit*. Visit the **Books with MyStatLab** section of the website at **www.mystatlab.com** for a complete list of package ISBNs.

How to Learn More about MyStatLab

- To learn more about MyStatLab, visit our website at **www.mystatlab.com**, or contact your Addison-Wesley sales representative to schedule a demonstration.
- For detailed instructions on how to register, log in, and set up your first MyStatLab course, view or print the *Getting Started with MyStatLab and CourseCompass* instructor guide from the **Support** section of the MyStatLab website at **www.mystatlab.com**.

Getting Started with MathXL for Statistics

Overview

MathXL® for Statistics is a powerful online homework, tutorial, and assessment system tied to Pearson Addison-Wesley and Pearson Prentice Hall textbooks in Mathematics and Statistics. Ideal for use in a lecture, self-paced, or distance-learning course, MathXL diagnoses students' weaknesses and creates a personalized study plan based on their test results. MathXL provides students with unlimited practice using a database of algorithmically-generated exercises correlated to the exercises in their textbook. Each tutorial exercise is accompanied by an interactive guided solution and a sample problem to help students improve their skills independently. Instructors can use MathXL to create online homework assignments, quizzes, and tests that are automatically graded and tracked. Instructors can view and manage all students' homework and test results, study plans, and tutorial work in MathXL's flexible online gradebook.

How to Adopt MathXL for Statistics

1. **Getting Access**
   If you are interested in using MathXL for one or more of your courses, contact your Addison-Wesley sales representative to request a *MathXL Instructor Access Kit*. (If you are not sure who your sales representative is, go to **www.aw-bc.com/replocator**.) The access kit provides you with an **instructor access code** for registration.

2. **Registering**
   Registering is an easy process that takes only a few minutes, and you need to register only once, even if you are teaching more than one course with MathXL. Detailed instructions are included in the instructor access kit. As part of the registration process, you select a login name and password that you will use from then on to access your MathXL course. Once you have your instructor access code, go to **www.mathxl.com**, click the **Register** button, and follow the on-screen instructions to register and log in.

3. **Creating Your MathXL Course**
   Once you've registered, creating your MathXL course is easy! Simply log in at **www.mathxl.com**, go to the Course Manager, and click Create Course. You will be asked to select the textbook you are using and enter some very basic information about your course. You can create as many courses as you need, and you can customize course coverage to match your syllabus if you wish.

4. **Ordering Books for Your Students**
   To access your MathXL course, each student needs to register in MathXL using a student access code. The easiest way to supply your students with access codes is to order your textbook packaged with the *MathXL Student Access Kit*. Visit the **Books with MathXL** section of the website at **www.mathxl.com** for a complete list of package ISBNs.

How to Learn More about MathXL for Statistics

- To learn more about MathXL, visit our website at **www.mathxl.com**, or contact your Addison-Wesley sales representative to schedule a demonstration.
- For detailed instructions on how to register, log in, and set up your first MathXL course, view or print the *Getting Started with MathXL* instructor guide from the **Support** section of the MathXL website at **www.mathxl.com**.

IX. Transition Guide

from Triola's *Elementary Statistics,* 9th edition
to Triola's *Elementary Statistics,* 10th edition

Statistical Methods, Procedures, and Notation: No changes from the 9th edition.

Organization: Section 2-3 (Visualizing Data) from the 9th edition has been divided into two sections: Section 2-3 (Histograms) and Section 2-4 (Statistical Graphics). Because of that change, Chapter 2 from the 9th edition has been divided into two chapters as shown below. Also because of that change, Chapters 4-14 from the 9th edition are now renumbered as Chapters 5-15 in the 10th edition.

9th edition		10th edition	
2-1	Overview	2-1	Overview
2-2	Frequency Distributions	2-2	Frequency Distributions
2-3	Visualizing Data →	2-3	Histograms
2-4	Measures of Center	2-4	Statistical Graphics
2-5	Measures of Variation		
2-6	Measures of Relative Standing		
2-7	Exploratory Data Analysis		
		3-1	Overview
		3-2	Measures of Center
		3-3	Measures of Variation
		3-4	Measures of Relative Standing
		3-5	Exploratory Data Analysis

New Sections

- Section 2-4: Statistical Graphics
- Section 11-4: McNemar's Test for Matched Pairs
- Section 4-8 (on the CD-ROM included with the book): Bayes' Theorem

Partitioned Sections: Each of the sections listed below has been partitioned into Part 1 (Basics) and Part 2 (Beyond the Basics) so that it is easier to focus on core concepts. It also becomes easier to exclude some topics that are not as important.

Section 3-2	Measures of Center
Section 3-3	Measures of Variation
Section 8-2	Basics of Hypothesis Testing
Section 9-3	Inferences About Two Means: Independent Samples
Section 10-2	Correlation
Section 10-3	Regression

(*continued*)

Expanded Coverage: Discussions on the following topics have been expanded.

Assessing normality with histograms (Section 2-3)
Statistical graphics (Section 2-4)
Power (Section 8-2)
Residual plots (Section 10-3)
Logistic regression (Section 10-5)
Multiple comparison procedures (Section 11-2)
Interactive plots (Section 12-3)

Requirement check: When appropriate, solutions to examples begin with a formal check of requirements that must be verified before a particular statistical method should be used. These requirement checks are set apart from the remainder of the solution.

Examples: 66% of the examples are new.

Exercises

- **Statistical Literacy and Critical Thinking:** Each set of section exercises now begins with four new exercises for **Statistical Literacy and Critical Thinking**. Also, the end of each chapter has a separate set of four such exercises.
- **Answers from technology:** The answers in Appendix E are based on the use of tables, but answers from technology are also included when there are discrepancies. For example, one answer is given as "*P*–value: 0.2743 (Tech: 0.2739)," where "Tech" indicates the answer that would be obtained by using a technology, such as STATDISK, Minitab, Excel, or a TI-83/84 Plus calculator.
- ***P*-values:** When applicable, *P*-values are now provided for almost all answers, so that professors or students can use the traditional method of hypothesis testing or the *P*-value method whenever they desire.
- **Smaller data sets:** The 10th edition has many more exercises that involve smaller data sets.
- **New exercises:** 68% of the exercises are new. 53% of the exercises use ***real data***.

Technology

STATDISK has many new features, such as the *Explore Data* function that automatically provides one screen showing statistics, confidence intervals, histogram, boxplot, and normal quantile plot for a list of data. Also new: McNemar's test, Fisher exact test, specificity, sensitivity, odds ratio, and relative risk. STATDISK 10.1 has been completely reprogrammed from Version 9.0, and it has been analyzed by several beta testers. STATDISK is free, it's easy, and it is on the CD included with each book.
DDXL is a new Version 2, including new functions such as rank correlation, chi-square test and confidence interval for one standard deviation, *F*-test for two standard deviations, chi-square goodness-of-fit test, chi-square test for a contingency table, sign test, Mann-Whitney test, and the Wilcoxon signed-ranks test.
Technologies used in 10th edition: Same as 9th edition (STATDISK, Minitab, Excel, TI-83/84 Plus calculator).

X. Bayes' Theorem

by Mario F. Triola

The concept of *conditional probability* is introduced in *Elementary Statistics.* We noted that the conditional probability of an event is a probability obtained with the additional information that some other event has already occurred. We used $P(B|A)$ to denoted the conditional probability of event B occurring, given that event A has already occurred. The following formula was provided for finding $P(B|A)$:

$$P(B|A) = \frac{P(A \text{ and } B)}{P(A)}$$

In addition to the above formal rule, the textbook also included this "intuitive approach for finding a conditional probability":

> The conditional probability of B given A can be found by assuming that event A has occurred and, working under that assumption, calculating the probability that event B will occur.

In this section we extend the discussion of conditional probability to include applications of *Bayes' theorem* (or *Bayes' rule*), which we use for revising a probability value based on additional information that is later obtained. One key to understanding the essence of Bayes' theorem is to recognize that we are dealing with *sequential* events, whereby new additional information is obtained for a subsequent event, and that new information is used to revise the probability of the initial event. In this context, the terms *prior probability* and *posterior probability* are commonly used.

Definitions

A **prior probability** is an initial probability value originally obtained before any additional information is obtained.
A **posterior probability** is a probability value that has been revised by using additional information that is later obtained.

Example 1

The Gallup organization randomly selects an adult American for a survey about credit card usage. Use subjective probabilities to estimate the following.

a. What is the probability that the selected subject is a male?

b. After selecting a subject, it is later learned that this person was smoking a cigar during the interview. What is the probability that the selected subject is a male?

c. Which of the preceding two results is a prior probability? Which is a posterior probability?

Solution

a. Roughly half of all Americans are males, so we estimate the probability of selecting a male subject to be 0.5. Denoting a male by M, we can express this probability as follows: $P(\text{M}) = 0.5$.

b. Although some women smoke cigars, the vast majority of cigar smokers are males. A reasonable guess is that 85% of cigar smokers are males. Based on this additional subsequent information that the survey respondent was smoking a cigar, we estimate the probability of this person being a male as 0.85. Denoting a male by M and denoting a cigar smoker by C, we can express this result as follows: $P(\text{M} \mid \text{C}) = 0.85$.

c. In part (a), the value of 0.5 is the initial probability, so we refer to it as the prior probability. Because the probability of 0.85 in part (b) is a revised probability based on the additional information that the survey subject was smoking a cigar, this value of 0.85 is referred to a posterior probability.

The Reverend Thomas Bayes [1701 (approximately) – 1761] was an English minister and mathematician. Although none of his work was published during his lifetime, later (posterior?) publications included the following theorem (or rule) that he developed for determining probabilities of events by incorporating information about subsequent events.

Bayes' Theorem

The probability of event *A,* given that event *B* has subsequently occurred, is

$$P(A|B) = \frac{P(A) \cdot P(B|A)}{[P(A) \cdot P(B|A)] + [P(\overline{A}) \cdot P(B|\overline{A})]}$$

That's a formidable expression, but we will simplify its calculation. See the following example, which illustrates use of the above expression, but also see the alternative method based on a more intuitive application of Bayes' theorem.

Example 2

In Orange County, 51% of the adults are males. (It doesn't take too much advanced mathematics to deduce that the other 49% are females.) One adult is randomly selected for a survey involving credit card usage.

a. Find the prior probability that the selected person is a male.

b. It is later learned that the selected survey subject was smoking a cigar. Also, 9.5% of males smoke cigars, whereas 1.7% of females smoke cigars (based on data from the Substance Abuse and Mental Health Services Administration). Use this additional information to find the probability that the selected subject is a male.

Solution

Let's use the following notation:

M = male $\overline{M}$ = female (or not male)

C = cigar smoker $\overline{C}$ = not a cigar smoker.

a. Before using the information given in part b, we know only that 51% of the adults in Orange County are males, so the probability of randomly selecting an adult and getting a male is given by $P(M) = 0.51$.

b. Based on the additional given information, we have the following:

$P(M) = 0.51$ because 51% of the adults are males

$P(\overline{M}) = 0.49$ because 49% of the adults are females (not males)

$P(C|M) = 0.095$ because 9.5% of the males smoke cigars (That is, the probability of getting someone who smokes cigars, given that the person is a male, is 0.095.)

$P(C|\overline{M}) = 0.017.$ because 1.7% of the females smoke cigars (That is, the probability of getting someone who smokes cigars, given that the person is a female, is 0.017.)

Let's now apply Bayes' theorem by using the preceding formula with M in place of A, and C in place of B. We get the following result:

$$P(M|C) = \frac{P(M)\cdot P(C|M)}{[P(M)\cdot P(C|M)]+[P(\overline{M})\cdot P(C|\overline{M})]}$$

$$= \frac{0.51\cdot 0.095}{[0.51\cdot 0.095]+[0.49\cdot 0.017]}$$

$$= 0.85329341$$

$$= 0.853 \text{ (rounded)}$$

Before we knew that the survey subject smoked a cigar, there is a 0.51 probability that the survey subject is male (because 51% of the adults in Orange County are males). However, after learning that the subject smoked a cigar, we revised the probability to 0.853. There is a 0.853 probability that the cigar–smoking respondent is a male. This makes sense, because the likelihood of a male increases dramatically with the additional information that the subject smokes cigars (because so many more males smoke cigars than females).

Intuitive Bayes Theorem

The preceding solution illustrates the application of Bayes' theorem with its calculation using the formula. Unfortunately, that calculation is complicated enough to create an abundance of opportunities for errors and/or incorrect substitution of the involved probability values. Fortunately, here is another approach that is much more intuitive and easier:

> **Assume some convenient value for the total of all items involved, then construct a table of rows and columns with the individual cell frequencies based on the known probabilities.**

For the preceding example, simply assume some value for the adult population of Orange County, such as 100,000, then use the given information to construct a table, such as the one shown below.

Finding the number of males who smoke cigars: If 51% of the 100,000 adults are males, then there are 51,000 males. If 9.5% of the males smoke cigars, then the number of cigar–smoking males is 9.5% of 51,000, or 0.095 × 51,000 = 4845. See the entry of 4845 in the table. The other males who do *not* smoke cigars must be 51,000 – 4845 = 46,155. See the value of 46,155 in the table.

Finding the number of females who smoke cigars: Using similar reasoning, 49% of the 100,000 adults are females, so the number of females is 49,000. Given that 1.7% of the females smoke cigars, the number of cigar–smoking females is 0.017 × 49,000 = 833. The number of females who do *not* smoke cigars is 49,000 – 833 = 48,167. See the entries of 833 and 48,167 in the table.

	C (Cigar Smoker)	$\overline{C}$ (Not a Cigar Smoker)	**Total**
M (male)	4845	46,155	**51,000**
$\overline{M}$ (female)	833	48,167	**49,000**
Total	**5678**	**94,322**	**100,000**

The above table involves relatively simple arithmetic. Simply partition the assumed population into the different cell categories by finding suitable percentages.

Now we can easily address the key question as follows: To find the probability of getting a male subject, given that the subject smokes cigars, simply use the same conditional probability described in the textbook. To find the probability of getting a male given that the subject smokes, restrict the table to the column of cigar smokers, then find the probability of getting a male in that column. Among the 5678 cigar smokers, there are 4845 males, so the probability we seek is 4845/5678 = 0.85329341. That is, $P(M \mid C) = 4845/5678 = 0.85329341 = 0.853$ (rounded).

Bayes' Theorem Generalized

The preceding formula for Bayes' theorem and the preceding example use exactly two categories for event *A* (male and female), but the formula can be extended to include more than two categories. The following example illustrates this extension and it also illustrates a practical application of Bayes' theorem to quality control in industry. When dealing with more than the two events of A and $\overline{A}$, we must be sure that the multiple events satisfy two important conditions:

1. The events must be *disjoint* (with no overlapping).

2. The events must be *exhaustive*, which means that they combine to include all possibilities.

Example 3

An aircraft emergency locator transmitter (ELT) is a device designed to transmit a signal in the case of a crash. The Altigauge Manufacturing Company makes 80% of the ELTs, the Bryant Company makes 15% of them, and the Chartair Company makes the other 5%. The ELTs made by Altigauge have a 4% rate of defects, the Bryant ELTs have a 6% rate of defects, and the Chartair ELTs have a 9% rate of defects (which helps to explain why Chartair has the lowest market share).

a. If an ELT is randomly selected from the general population of all ELTs, find the probability that it was made by the Altigauge Manufacturing Company.

b. If a randomly selected ELT is then tested and is found to be defective, find the probability that it was made by the Altigauge Manufacturing Company.

Solution

We use the following notation:

A = ELT manufactured by Altigauge
B = ELT manufactured by Bryant
C = ELT manufactured by Chartair

D = ELT is defective
$\overline{D}$ = ELT is not defective (or it is good)

a. If an ELT is randomly selected from the general population of all ELTs, the probability that it was made by Altigauge is 0.8 (because Altigauge manufactures 80% of them).

b. If we now have the additional information that the ELT was tested and was found to be defective, we want to revise the probability from part (a) so that the new information can be used. We want to find the value of $P(A|D)$, which is the probability that the ELT was made by the Altigauge company given that it is defective. Based on the given information, we know these probabilities:

$P(\text{A}) = 0.80$ because Altigauge makes 80% of the ELTs
$P(\text{B}) = 0.15$ because Bryant makes 15% of the ELTs
$P(\text{C}) = 0.05$ because Chartair makes 5% of the ELTs

$P(\text{D}|\text{A}) = 0.04$ because 4% of the Altigauge ELTs are defective
$P(\text{D}|\text{B}) = 0.06$ because 6% of the Bryant ELTs are defective
$P(\text{D}|\text{C}) = 0.09$ because 9% of the Chartair ELTs are defective

Here is Bayes' theorem extended to include three events corresponding to the selection of ELTs from the three manufacturers (A, B, C):

$$P(A|D) = \frac{P(A)\cdot P(D|A)}{[P(A)\cdot P(D|A)]+[P(B)\cdot P(D|B)]+[P(C)\cdot P(D|C)]}$$

$$= \frac{0.80\cdot 0.04}{[0.80\cdot 0.04]+[0.15\cdot 0.06]+[0.05\cdot 0.09]}$$

$$= 0.703 \text{ (rounded)}$$

Intuitive Baye's Theorem: Now let's find $P(\text{A}|\text{D})$ by using a table. Let's arbitrarily assume that 10,000 ELTs were manufactured. (The solution doesn't depend on the number selected, but it's helpful to select a number large enough so that the cells in the table are all whole numbers.) Because 80% of the ELTs are made by Altigauge, we have 8000 ELTs made by Altigauge, and 4% of them (or 320) are defective. Also, if 320 of the Altigauge ELTs are defective, the other 7680 are not defective. See the values of 320 and 7680 in the table below. The other values are found using the same reasoning.

	D (defective)	$\overline{\text{D}}$ (not defective)	**Total**
A (Altigauge)	320	7680	**8,000**
B (Bryant)	90	1410	**1,500**
C (Chartair)	45	455	**500**
Total	**455**	**9545**	**10,000**

We want to find the probability that an ELT was made by Altigauge, given that it is known to be defective. Because we know the condition that the ELT is defective, we can refer to the first column of values where we see that among the 455 total defective ELTs, 320 were made by Altigauge, so that the probability is 320/455 = 0.703 (rounded). This is the same result obtained with the formula from Bayes' theorem.

The preceding example involve an extension of Bayes' theorem to three events denoted by A, B, C. Based on the format of the formula used in the solution, it is easy to extend Bayes' theorem so that it can be used with four or more events. (See Exercises 11 and 12.)

Exercises

Pregnancy Test Results. *In Exercises 1 and 2, refer to the results summarized in the table below.*

	Positive Test Result (Pregnancy is indicated)	Negative Test Result (Pregnancy is not indicated)
Subject is Pregnant	80	5
Subject is Not Pregnant	3	11

1. a. If one of the 99 test subjects is randomly selected, what is the probability of getting a subject who is pregnant?

b. A test subject is randomly selected and is given a pregnancy test. What is the probability of getting a subject who is pregnant, given that the test result is positive?

2. a. One of the 99 test subjects is randomly selected. What is the probability of getting a subject who is not pregnant?

b. A test subject is randomly selected and is given a pregnancy test. What is the probability of getting a subject who is not pregnant, given that the test result is negative?

3. ***Survey Results*** In Orange County, 51% of the adults are males. One adult is randomly selected for a survey involving credit card usage. (See Example 2 in this section.)

a. Find the prior probability that the selected person is a female.

b. It is later learned that the selected survey subject was smoking a cigar. Also, 9.5% of males smoke cigars, whereas 1.7% of females smoke cigars (based on data from the Substance Abuse and Mental Health Services Administration). Use this additional information to find the probability that the selected subject is a female.

4. ***Emergency Locator Transmitters*** An aircraft emergency locator transmitter (ELT) is a device designed to transmit a signal in the case of a crash. The Altigauge Manufacturing Company makes 80% of the ELTs, the Bryant Company makes 15% of them, and the Chartair Company makes the other 5%. The ELTs made by Altigauge have a 4% rate of defects, the Bryant ELTs have a 6% rate of defects, and the Chartair ELTs have a 9% rate of defects. (These are the same results from Example 3 in this section.)

a. Find the probability of randomly selecting an ELT and getting one manufactured by the Bryant Company.

b. If an ELT is randomly selected and tested, find the probability that it was manufactured by the Bryant Company if the test indicates that the ELT is defective.

5. ***Emergency Locator Transmitters*** Use the same ELT data from Exercise 4.

a. Find the probability of randomly selecting an ELT and getting one manufactured by the Chartair Company.

b. An ELT is randomly selected and tested. If the test indicates that the ELT is defective, find the probability that it was manufactured by the Chartair Company.

6. ***Emergency Locator Transmitters*** Use the same ELT data from Exercise 4. An ELT is randomly selected and tested. If the test indicates that the ELT is *not* defective, find the probability that it is from the Altigauge Company.

7. ***Pleas and Sentences*** In a study of pleas and prison sentences, it is found that 45% of the subjects studied were sent to prison. Among those sent to prison, 40% chose to plead guilty. Among those not sent to prison, 55% chose to plead guilty.

a. If one of the study subjects is randomly selected, find the probability of getting someone who was not sent to prison.

b. If a study subject is randomly selected and it is then found that the subject entered a guilty plea, find the probability that this person was not sent to prison.

8. ***Pleas and Sentences*** Use the same data given in Exercise 7.

a. If one of the study subjects is randomly selected, find the probability of getting someone who was sent to prison.

b. If a study subject is randomly selected and it is then found that the subject entered a guilty plea, find the probability that this person was sent to prison.

9. ***HIV*** The New York State Health Department reports a 10% rate of the HIV virus for the "at-risk" population. Under certain conditions, a preliminary screening test for the HIV virus is correct 95% of the time. (Subjects are not told that they are HIV infected until additional tests verify the results.) If someone is randomly selected from the at-risk population, what is the probability that they have the HIV virus if it is known that they have tested positive in the initial screening?

10. ***HIV*** Use the same data from Exercise 9. If someone is randomly selected from the at-risk population, what is the probability that they have the HIV virus if it is known that they have tested negative in the initial screening?

11. ***Extending Bayes' Theorem*** Example 3 in this section included an extension of Bayes' theorem to include three events, denoted by A, B, C. Write an expression that extends Bayes' theorem so that it can be used to find $P(A|Z)$, assuming that the initial event can occur in one of four ways: A, B, C, D.

12. ***Extensions of Bayes' Theorem*** In Example 2, we used only the initial events of A and $\overline{A}$. In Example 3, we used initial events of A, B, and C. If events B and C in Example 3 are combined and denoted as $\overline{A}$, we can find $P(A|D)$ using the simpler format of Bayes' theorem given in Example 2. How would the resulting value of $P(A|D)$ in Example 3 be affected by using this simplified approach?

Answers to Exercises

1. a. 85/99 or 0.859

   b. 80/83 or 0.964

2. a. 14/99 or 0.141

   b. 11/16 or 0.688

3. a. 0.49

   b. 0.147

4. a. 0.15

   b. 0.198

5. a. 0.05

   b. 0.0989

6. 0.805

7. a. 0.55

   b. 0.627

8. a. 0.45

   b. 0.373

9. 0.679

10. 0.00581

11. $$P(A|Z) = \frac{P(A) \cdot P(Z|A)}{[P(A) \cdot P(Z|A)] + [P(B) \cdot P(Z|B)] + [P(C) \cdot P(Z|C)] + [P(D) \cdot P(Z|D)]}$$

12. Results are the same.

XI. Extra Data Sets

The following pages list these extra data sets, which are available on the CD-ROM included in the textbook. These data sets are available on the CD-ROM as a Word document or in a rich-text format.

BLOOD

BOOKS

CARS

CEREAL

EVERGLADES

HEIGHTS

IRIS

MARATHON

MISC

MOVIES

OLDHOMES

OLDM&M

OLDOLDFAITHFUL

QWERTY

STOWAWAYS

SURVEY

SYSTOLIC

YEAST

BLOOD: The data are blood measurements from 50 subjects (from the U.S. Department of Health and Human Services, National Center for Health Statistics, Third National Health and Nutrition Examination Survey). The gender, age, white blood cell count, red blood cell count, hemoglobin level, and platelet count are given for each subject. The blood cell counts are easured in cells per microliter; hemoglobin is measured in g/dL; platelet count is number per mm^3.

Sex	Age	White bcc	Red bcc	Hemoglobin	Platelets
F	30	8.9	4.39	13.5	224
M	29	5.25	5.18	15.9	264.5
M	21	5.95	4.88	13.9	360
M	33	10.05	5.94	15.85	384.5
F	24	6.5	4.48	13.55	364.5
F	28	9.45	3.58	10.95	468
M	57	5.45	4.4	12.5	171
M	28	5.3	4.88	15.6	328.5
F	48	7.65	4.22	13.05	323.5
F	60	6.4	4.36	12.2	306.5
F	20	5.15	4.59	14.25	264.5
F	19	16.6	3.63	11.5	233
F	53	5.75	4.54	14	254.5
M	34	5.55	4.92	14.05	267
F	26	11.6	3.92	11.4	463
M	18	6.85	5.44	14.65	238
M	26	6.65	5.07	15.4	251
F	25	5.9	4.24	12.8	282.5
F	48	9.3	4.21	14.3	307.5
M	24	6.3	4.8	14.7	321.5
F	48	8.55	5.06	14.9	360.5
M	28	6.4	5.14	15.2	282.5
F	52	10.8	4.71	14.9	315
F	32	4.85	4.23	11.5	284
F	46	4.9	4.68	14.45	259.5
M	20	7.85	5.99	14.05	291.5
F	23	8.75	3.83	12.2	259.5
M	26	7.7	4.82	15.35	164
M	27	5.3	4.57	14.15	199.5
M	46	6.5	4.59	14.5	220
F	37	6.9	3.95	11.1	369
M	27	4.55	4.77	14.85	245
M	25	7.1	5.12	14.6	266
M	55	8	5.37	15.6	369
M	27	4.7	5.17	15.45	210.5
M	53	4.4	4.97	14.6	234
F	50	9.75	3.87	12.75	471
M	18	4.9	4.8	15.2	244.5
M	36	10.75	5.05	15.65	365.5
M	52	11	5.11	15.3	265

F	29	4.05	4.2	12.75	198
F	31	9.05	4.07	13.1	390
F	17	5.05	3.74	11.4	269.5
F	24	6.4	4.72	13.3	344.5
F	37	4.05	4.63	13.7	386.5
F	48	7.6	4.63	15.1	256
F	23	4.95	4.3	13.55	226
M	45	9.6	5.13	15.95	225
F	21	3	4.07	11.9	259
F	22	9.1	4.6	14.2	271.5

BOOKS: From 12 pages randomly selected from each of three books: *The Bear and the Dragon* by Tom Clancy, *Harry Potter and the Sorcerer's Stone* by J. K. Rowling, and *War and Peace* by Leo Tolstoy.

Clancy:

Words/sentence	Characters/word	Flesch Reading Ease	Flesch-Kincaid Grade Level
15.0	4.8	58.2	8.8
9.8	4.5	73.4	5.4
8.1	4.6	73.1	5.0
13.5	4.5	64.4	7.6
24.0	4.0	72.7	9.0
9.8	4.0	89.2	3.2
33.0	4.6	43.9	12.0
9.4	4.5	76.3	4.9
8.3	4.4	76.4	4.6
11.3	4.4	78.9	5.0
11.4	4.3	69.4	6.4
12.4	4.3	72.9	6.1

ROWLING:

Words/sentence	Characters/word	Flesch Reading Ease	Flesch-Kincaid Grade Level
15.7	4.1	85.3	5.2
9.0	4.2	84.3	3.7
16.3	4.2	79.5	6.1
14.5	4.4	82.5	4.9
9.7	4.3	80.2	4.4
7.4	4.2	84.6	3.2
14.0	4.5	79.2	5.6
16.1	4.5	70.9	6.9
13.9	4.3	78.6	5.7
12.5	4.0	86.2	4.1
17.2	4.4	74.0	6.7
11.5	4.3	83.7	4.4

TOLSTOY:

Words/sentence	Characters/word	Flesch Reading Ease	Flesch-Kincaid Grade Level
20.6	4.3	69.4	8.6
28.0	4.5	64.2	9.8
12.0	4.5	71.4	6.1
11.5	4.5	71.6	5.9
17.4	4.5	68.5	7.7
19.7	4.8	51.9	10.9
20.3	4.3	72.2	8.2
17.8	4.2	74.4	7.2
22.1	4.7	52.8	11.0
31.4	4.3	58.4	11.5
18.3	4.4	65.4	8.4
11.7	4.5	73.6	5.9

CARS: A sample of 20 cars, including measurements of fuel consumption (city mi/gal and highway mi/gal), weight (pounds), number of cylinders, engine displacement (in liters), amount of greenhouse gases emitted (in tons/year), and amount of tailpipe emissions of NO_x (in lb/yr).

CAR	CITY	HWY	WEIGHT	CYL	DISP.	MAN/AUTO	GHG	NOX
Chev. Camaro	19	30	3545	6	3.8	M	12	34.4
Chev. Cavalier	23	31	2795	4	2.2	A	10	25.1
Dodge Neon	23	32	2600	4	2	A	10	25.1
Ford Taurus	19	27	3515	6	3	A	12	25.1
Honda Accord	23	30	3245	4	2.3	A	11	25.1
Lincoln Cont.	17	24	3930	8	4.6	A	14	25.1
Mercury Mystique	20	29	3115	6	2.5	A	12	34.4
Mitsubishi Eclipse	22	33	3235	4	2	M	10	25.1
Olds. Aurora	17	26	3995	8	4	A	13	34.4
Pontiac Grand Am	22	30	3115	4	2.4	A	11	25.1
Toyota Camry	23	32	3240	4	2.2	M	10	25.1
Cadillac DeVille	17	26	4020	8	4.6	A	13	34.4
Chev. Corvette	18	28	3220	8	5.7	M	12	34.4
Chrysler Sebring	19	27	3175	6	2.5	A	12	25.1
Ford Mustang	20	29	3450	6	3.8	M	12	34.4
BMW 3-Series	19	27	3225	6	2.8	A	12	34.4
Ford Crown Victoria	17	24	3985	8	4.6	A	14	25.1
Honda Civic	32	37	2440	4	1.6	M	8	25.1
Mazda Protege	29	34	2500	4	1.6	A	9	25.1
Hyundai Accent	28	37	2290	4	1.5	A	9	34.4

CEREAL: Data from 16 brands of cereal, including cost per 100 grams, and the contents of calories, fat, sugar, cholesterol, sodium, protein, and the shelf on which the cereal was placed.

Cereal	Cost ($) per 100 grams of cereal	Calories per gram of cereal	Grams of fat per gram of cereal	Grams of sugar per gram of cereal	Chol. per gram of cereal	Sodium (mg) per gram of cereal	Protein (g) per gram of cereal	Shelf Loc.
Cheerios	0.67	3.7	0.07	0.03	0	9.3	0.10	1
Harmony	0.82	3.6	0.02	0.24	0	6.4	0.09	3
Smart Start	0.78	3.6	0.01	0.30	0	6.6	0.06	4
Cocoa Puffs	1.03	4.0	0.03	0.47	0	5.7	0.03	2
Lucky Charms	0.83	4.0	0.03	0.43	0	7.0	0.07	2
Corn Flakes	0.55	3.6	0.00	0.07	0	7.1	0.07	1
Fruit Loops	0.68	3.8	0.03	0.47	0	4.7	0.03	2
Wheaties	0.78	3.7	0.03	0.13	0	7.3	0.10	1
Cap'n Crunch	0.73	4.1	0.06	0.44	0	7.4	0.04	1
Frosted Flakes	0.65	3.9	0.00	0.39	0	4.8	0.03	1
Apple Jacks	0.81	3.9	0.02	0.48	0	4.5	0.03	2
Bran Flakes	0.70	3.3	0.02	0.17	0	7.0	0.10	4
Special K	0.78	3.5	0.00	0.13	0	7.1	0.23	1
Rice Krispies	0.95	3.6	0.00	0.09	0	9.7	0.06	4
Corn Pops	0.84	3.9	0.00	0.45	0	3.9	0.03	2
Trix	0.94	4.0	0.03	0.43	0	6.3	0.03	2

EVERGLADES: Temperatures (in degrees Celsius), conductivity measurements, and rainfall amounts (in inches) are given for the Garfield Bight hydrology outpost in the Florida Everglades. The data are from Kevin Kotun and the National Park Service.

Bottom Temp (Celsius)	Conductivity	Rainfall (inches)
27.6	57.8	0.10
29.1	57.8	0.17
29.4	57.1	0.65
28.5	57.0	0.00
28.6	57.3	0.00
28.0	58.4	0.00
27.9	59.2	0.65
29.0	57.7	0.00
30.6	56.8	0.67
31.2	56.8	0.03
30.7	55.2	1.72
28.0	53.6	0.00
28.3	52.0	0.84
30.1	51.9	0.00
31.3	49.8	0.00
31.0	49.8	0.06
30.8	51.7	0.50
28.5	48.6	1.50
25.9	44.3	1.40
28.5	43.2	0.00
31.9	41.5	0.00
31.3	40.6	0.18
29.4	35.9	2.77
30.0	33.8	0.04
30.1	32.8	0.00
28.8	30.5	1.11
29.5	32.7	0.00
30.5	32.1	0.04
29.2	30.3	1.72
28.8	28.1	0.00
30.1	29.3	0.05
29.2	30.2	0.07
28.2	33.5	0.03
29.1	40.5	0.00
29.9	42.4	0.01
29.9	46.7	0.00
30.6	46.7	0.00
30.6	46.5	0.00
30.9	45.6	0.00
30.0	47.1	0.00

continued

Bottom Temp (Celsius)	Conductivity	Rainfall (inches)
30.7	48.1	0.00
31.9	50.5	0.00
31.5	51.2	0.02
31.2	50.4	0.00
30.9	49.9	0.94
30.6	49.0	0.00
30.1	48.5	0.38
31.1	51.3	0.05
31.5	52.1	0.34
31.8	52.4	0.02
32.0	51.0	0.00
32.6	52.2	0.34
32.9	50.3	0.02
32.7	48.5	0.00
33.5	49.7	0.00
33.8	49.9	0.09
33.7	48.5	0.00
33.6	48.3	0.00
32.3	49.0	0.00
31.6	49.9	0.00
32.0	51.0	0.00

HEIGHTS: The data are heights of 20 boys and 20 girls along with the heights of both parents. All heights are in inches. The data are from the U.S. Department of Health and Human Services, National Center for Health Statistics, Third National Health and Nutrition Examination Survey.

Gender	Height	Mother's Height	Father's Height
M	62.5	66	70
M	64.6	58	69
M	69.1	66	64
M	73.9	68	71
M	67.1	64	68
M	64.4	62	66
M	71.1	66	74
M	71.0	63	73
M	67.4	64	62
M	69.3	65	69
M	64.9	64	67
M	68.1	64	68
M	66.5	62	72
M	67.5	69	66
M	66.5	62	72
M	70.3	67	68
M	67.5	63	71
M	68.5	66	67
M	71.9	65	71
M	67.8	71	75
F	58.6	63	64
F	64.7	67	65
F	65.3	64	67
F	61.0	60	72
F	65.4	65	72
F	67.4	67	72
F	60.9	59	67
F	63.1	60	71
F	60.0	58	66
F	71.1	72	75
F	62.2	63	69
F	67.2	67	70
F	63.4	62	69
F	68.4	69	62
F	62.2	63	66
F	64.7	64	76
F	59.6	63	69
F	61.0	64	68
F	64.0	60	66
F	65.4	65	68

IRIS: The data are 50 measurements (sepal length, sepal width, petal length, petal width) from each of three classes (setosa, versicolor, virginica) of Irises. The data are from "The Use of Multiple Measurements in Taxonomic Problems" by R.A. Fisher, *Annals of Statistics*, Vol. 7. All measurements are in mm.

CLASS	SepLnght	SepWdth	PetLngth	PetWdth
setosa	5.1	3.5	1.4	0.2
setosa	4.9	3	1.4	0.2
setosa	4.7	3.2	1.3	0.2
setosa	4.6	3.1	1.5	0.2
setosa	5	3.6	1.4	0.2
setosa	5.4	3.9	1.7	0.4
setosa	4.6	3.4	1.4	0.3
setosa	5	3.4	1.5	0.2
setosa	4.4	2.9	1.4	0.2
setosa	4.9	3.1	1.5	0.1
setosa	5.4	3.7	1.5	0.2
setosa	4.8	3.4	1.6	0.2
setosa	4.8	3	1.4	0.1
setosa	4.3	3	1.1	0.1
setosa	5.8	4	1.2	0.2
setosa	5.7	4.4	1.5	0.4
setosa	5.4	3.9	1.3	0.4
setosa	5.1	3.5	1.4	0.3
setosa	5.7	3.8	1.7	0.3
setosa	5.1	3.8	1.5	0.3
setosa	5.4	3.4	1.7	0.2
setosa	5.1	3.7	1.5	0.4
setosa	4.6	3.6	1	0.2
setosa	5.1	3.3	1.7	0.5
setosa	4.8	3.4	1.9	0.2
setosa	5	3	1.6	0.2
setosa	5	3.4	1.6	0.4
setosa	5.2	3.5	1.5	0.2
setosa	5.2	3.4	1.4	0.2
setosa	4.7	3.2	1.6	0.2
setosa	4.8	3.1	1.6	0.2
setosa	5.4	3.4	1.5	0.4
setosa	5.2	4.1	1.5	0.1
setosa	5.5	4.2	1.4	0.2
setosa	4.9	3.1	1.5	0.1
setosa	5	3.2	1.2	0.2
setosa	5.5	3.5	1.3	0.2
setosa	4.9	3.1	1.5	0.1
setosa	4.4	3	1.3	0.2

continued

CLASS	SepLnght	SepWdth	PetLngth	PetWdth
setosa	5.1	3.4	1.5	0.2
setosa	5	3.5	1.3	0.3
setosa	4.5	2.3	1.3	0.3
setosa	4.4	3.2	1.3	0.2
setosa	5	3.5	1.6	0.6
setosa	5.1	3.8	1.9	0.4
setosa	4.8	3	1.4	0.3
setosa	5.1	3.8	1.6	0.2
setosa	4.6	3.2	1.4	0.2
setosa	5.3	3.7	1.5	0.2
setosa	5	3.3	1.4	0.2
versicolor	7	3.2	4.7	1.4
versicolor	6.4	3.2	4.5	1.5
versicolor	6.9	3.1	4.9	1.5
versicolor	5.5	2.3	4	1.3
versicolor	6.5	2.8	4.6	1.5
versicolor	5.7	2.8	4.5	1.3
versicolor	6.3	3.3	4.7	1.6
versicolor	4.9	2.4	3.3	1
versicolor	6.6	2.9	4.6	1.3
versicolor	5.2	2.7	3.9	1.4
versicolor	5	2	3.5	1
versicolor	5.9	3	4.2	1.5
versicolor	6	2.2	4	1
versicolor	6.1	2.9	4.7	1.4
versicolor	5.6	2.9	3.6	1.3
versicolor	6.7	3.1	4.4	1.4
versicolor	5.6	3	4.5	1.5
versicolor	5.8	2.7	4.1	1
versicolor	6.2	2.2	4.5	1.5
versicolor	5.6	2.5	3.9	1.1
versicolor	5.9	3.2	4.8	1.8
versicolor	6.1	2.8	4	1.3
versicolor	6.3	2.5	4.9	1.5
versicolor	6.1	2.8	4.7	1.2
versicolor	6.4	2.9	4.3	1.3
versicolor	6.6	3	4.4	1.4
versicolor	6.8	2.8	4.8	1.4
versicolor	6.7	3	5	1.7
versicolor	6	2.9	4.5	1.5
versicolor	5.7	2.6	3.5	1
versicolor	5.5	2.4	3.8	1.1
versicolor	5.5	2.4	3.7	1
versicolor	5.8	2.7	3.9	1.2
versicolor	6	2.7	5.1	1.6
versicolor	5.4	3	4.5	1.5

continued

CLASS	SepLnght	SepWdth	PetLngth	PetWdth
versicolor	6.7	3.1	4.7	1.5
versicolor	6.3	2.3	4.4	1.3
versicolor	5.6	3	4.1	1.3
versicolor	5.5	2.5	4	1.3
versicolor	5.5	2.6	4.4	1.2
versicolor	6.1	3	4.6	1.4
versicolor	5.8	2.6	4	1.2
versicolor	5	2.3	3.3	1
versicolor	5.6	2.7	4.2	1.3
versicolor	5.7	3	4.2	1.2
versicolor	5.7	2.9	4.2	1.3
versicolor	6.2	2.9	4.3	1.3
versicolor	5.1	2.5	3	1.1
versicolor	5.7	2.8	4.1	1.3
virginica	6.3	3.3	6	2.5
virginica	5.8	2.7	5.1	1.9
virginica	7.1	3	5.9	2.1
virginica	6.3	2.9	5.6	1.8
virginica	6.5	3	5.8	2.2
virginica	7.6	3	6.6	2.1
virginica	4.9	2.5	4.5	1.7
virginica	7.3	2.9	6.3	1.8
virginica	6.7	2.5	5.8	1.8
virginica	7.2	3.6	6.1	2.5
virginica	6.5	3.2	5.1	2
virginica	6.4	2.7	5.3	1.9
virginica	6.8	3	5.5	2.1
virginica	5.7	2.5	5	2
virginica	5.8	2.8	5.1	2.4
virginica	6.4	3.2	5.3	2.3
virginica	6.5	3	5.5	1.8
virginica	7.7	3.8	6.7	2.2
virginica	7.7	2.6	6.9	2.3
virginica	6	2.2	5	1.5
virginica	6.9	3.2	5.7	2.3
virginica	5.6	2.8	4.9	2
virginica	7.7	2.8	6.7	2
virginica	6.3	2.7	4.9	1.8
virginica	6.7	3.3	5.7	2.1
virginica	7.2	3.2	6	1.8
virginica	6.2	2.8	4.8	1.8
virginica	6.1	3	4.9	1.8
virginica	6.4	2.8	5.6	2.1
virginica	7.2	3	5.8	1.6

continued

CLASS	SepLnght	SepWdth	PetLngth	PetWdth
virginica	7.4	2.8	6.1	1.9
virginica	7.9	3.8	6.4	2
virginica	6.4	2.8	5.6	2.2
virginica	6.3	2.8	5.1	1.5
virginica	6.1	2.6	5.6	1.4
virginica	7.7	3	6.1	2.3
virginica	6.3	3.4	5.6	2.4
virginica	6.4	3.1	5.5	1.8
virginica	6	3	4.8	1.8
virginica	6.9	3.1	5.4	2.1
virginica	6.7	3.1	5.6	2.4
virginica	6.9	3.1	5.1	2.3
virginica	5.8	2.7	5.1	1.9
virginica	6.8	3.2	5.9	2.3
virginica	6.7	3.3	5.7	2.5
virginica	6.7	3	5.2	2.3
virginica	6.3	2.5	5	1.9
virginica	6.5	3	5.2	2
virginica	6.2	3.4	5.4	2.3
virginica	5.9	3	5.1	1.8

MARATHON: The data are 150 randomly-selected results for 150 runners who finished the New York City Marathon in a recent year. For each subject, the order, age, gender, and time (in seconds) are given.

Order	Age	Gender	Time (sec)
130	32	M	9631
265	39	M	10209
314	39	M	10351
490	36	M	10641
547	34	M	10723
708	28	M	10905
834	42	M	11061
944	46	M	11188
1084	32	M	11337
1086	34	M	11338
1132	41	M	11382
1593	36	M	11738
1625	50	M	11761
1735	36	M	11830
1792	40	M	11874
1826	33	M	11897
2052	29	F	12047
2108	28	M	12077
2167	40	M	12115
2505	30	F	12289
2550	28	M	12312
3344	44	M	12639
3376	45	M	12652
4115	45	M	12940
4252	54	M	12986
4459	33	M	13063
4945	49	M	13217
5269	45	M	13315
5286	40	M	13322
5559	26	M	13408
6169	23	F	13593
6235	21	M	13615
6552	50	F	13704
6618	33	M	13722
6904	38	M	13802
6996	40	M	13829
7082	38	M	13851
7093	32	F	13854
7933	50	M	14057
7966	43	M	14066
8011	25	M	14078
8027	39	M	14082
8042	31	M	14086
8186	37	M	14121

8225	16	M	14128
8609	23	F	14216
8707	30	F	14235
8823	24	M	14256
9451	29	M	14375
9630	30	M	14402
10130	36	M	14512
10191	40	M	14528
10556	51	M	14617
10585	51	M	14623
10643	51	M	14632
10821	30	M	14677
10910	38	M	14698
10979	59	M	14720
10982	28	F	14721
11091	49	M	14752
11413	55	M	14836
11699	53	M	14919
11769	53	M	14935
11792	40	M	14942
11869	38	M	14964
11896	35	M	14971
11997	54	M	14996
12019	21	M	15002
12160	33	F	15036
12306	58	F	15077
12683	43	M	15167
12845	33	M	15210
12942	35	M	15232
13226	31	M	15309
13262	38	M	15318
13297	28	F	15326
13434	30	F	15357
13597	23	F	15402
14391	40	M	15608
14633	43	M	15671
14909	43	M	15741
15282	29	M	15825
16030	34	F	16013
16324	30	M	16090
16723	65	M	16194
16840	50	M	16229
17104	37	F	16297
17298	30	F	16352
17436	32	M	16389
17483	19	F	16401
17487	42	M	16402
17694	33	M	16461
18132	42	M	16582
18765	51	M	16752

18783	54	F	16758
18825	32	F	16771
18897	34	F	16792
19002	31	M	16812
19210	50	F	16871
19264	60	M	16886
19278	49	M	16889
19649	51	F	16991
19789	45	M	17034
20425	40	F	17211
20558	30	M	17245
20562	25	M	17246
20580	32	M	17252
20592	34	M	17257
20605	42	F	17260
20700	34	F	17286
20826	52	M	17327
21013	38	M	17396
21017	47	M	17397
21524	34	M	17563
21787	37	F	17636
22009	37	M	17711
22042	31	F	17726
22258	29	F	17799
22285	49	M	17807
22638	31	M	17918
22993	52	M	18041
23092	38	M	18080
24018	30	F	18469
24283	31	F	18580
24290	40	M	18583
24417	50	F	18647
24466	29	M	18677
24649	21	M	18784
24845	53	M	18906
25262	41	M	19164
25287	50	F	19177
25956	45	M	19669
26471	27	F	20084
26545	32	M	20164
26637	53	M	20269
27035	42	F	20675
27046	45	M	20698
27133	39	M	20808
27152	31	M	20841
27196	68	F	20891
27277	51	M	20970
27800	51	M	21649
27955	31	F	21911
27995	25	F	21983

28062	25	M	22087
28085	61	M	22146
28578	31	M	23545
28779	32	M	24384
28986	47	F	25399
29045	61	F	25898

MISC: These data for the years 1980-2000: Dow Jones Industrial Average high level, U.S. car sales (in thousands), U.S. motor vehicle deaths, U.S. murders and non-negligent homicides, sunspot number, total points scored in the Super Bowl.

Year	DJIA High	US Car Sales (thousands)	US Motor Vehicle Deaths	US Murders and Non-Negligent Homicides	Sunspot Number	Super Bowl Points
1980	1000	8979	53172	23040	154.6	50
1981	1024	8536	51385	22520	140.5	37
1982	1071	7982	45779	21010	115.9	57
1983	1287	9182	44452	19310	66.6	44
1984	1287	10390	46263	18690	45.9	47
1985	1553	11042	45901	18980	17.9	54
1986	1956	11460	47865	20610	13.4	56
1987	2722	10277	48290	20100	29.2	59
1988	2184	10530	49078	20680	100.2	36
1989	2791	9773	47575	21500	157.6	65
1990	3000	9300	46814	23440	142.6	39
1991	3169	8175	43536	24700	145.7	61
1992	3413	8213	40982	23760	94.3	69
1993	3794	8518	41893	24530	54.6	43
1994	3978	8991	42524	23330	29.9	75
1995	5216	8635	43363	21610	17.5	44
1996	6561	8527	43649	19650	8.6	56
1997	8259	8272	43458	18210	21.5	55
1998	9374	8142	43501	16970	64.3	53
1999	11568	8698	41300	15522	93.3	39
2000	11401	8847	43000	15517	119.6	41

MOVIES: A sample of 36 movies including the budget amounts (in millions of dollars), the amounts grossed (in millions of dollars), the lengths of the movies (in minutes), and the viewer ratings.

Title	Year	Rating	Budget ($) in Millions	Gross ($) in Millions	Length (Minutes)	Viewer Rating
Aliens	1986	R	18.5	81.843	137	8.2
Armageddon	1998	PG-13	140	194.125	144	6.7
As Good As It Gets	1997	PG-13	50	147.54	138	8.1
Braveheart	1995	R	72	75.6	177	8.3
Chasing Amy	1997	R	0.25	12.006	105	7.9
Contact	1997	PG	90	100.853	153	8.3
Dante's Peak	1997	PG-13	104	67.155	112	6.7
Deep Impact	1998	PG-13	75	140.424	120	6.4
Executive Decision	1996	R	55	68.75	129	7.3
Forrest Gump	1994	PG-13	55	329.691	142	7.7
Ghost	1990	PG-13	22	217.631	128	7.1
Gone with the Wind	1939	G	3.9	198.571	222	8
Good Will Hunting	1997	R	10	138.339	126	8.5
Grease	1978	PG	6	181.28	110	7.3
Halloween	1978	R	0.325	47	93	7.7
Hard Rain	1998	R	70	19.819	95	5.2
I Know What You Did Last Summer	1997	R	17	72.219	100	6.5
Independence Day	1996	PG-13	75	306.124	142	6.6
Indiana Jones and the Last Crusade	1989	PG-13	39	197.171	127	7.8
Jaws	1975	PG	12	260	124	7.8
Men in Black	1997	PG-13	90	250.147	98	7.4
Multiplicity	1996	PG-13	45	20.1	117	6.8
Pulp Fiction	1994	R	8	107.93	154	8.3
Raiders of the Lost Ark	1981	PG	20	242.374	115	8.3
Saving Private ryan	1998	R	70	178.091	170	9.1
Schindler's List	1993	R	25	96.067	197	8.6
Scream	1996	R	15	103.001	111	7.7
Speed 2:Cruise Control	1997	PG-13	110	48.068	121	4.3
Terminator	1984	R	6.4	36.9	108	7.7
The American President	1995	PG-13	62	65	114	7.6
The Fifth Element	1997	PG-13	90	63.54	126	7.8
The Game	1997	R	50	48.265	128	7.6
The Man in the Iron Mask	1998	PG-13	35	56.876	132	6.5
Titanic	1997	PG-13	200	600.743	195	8.4
True Lies	1994	R	100	146.261	144	7.2
Volcano	1997	PG-13	90	47.474	102	5.8

OLDHOMES: Data Set 18 in the 10th edition of *Elementary Statistics* includes recent data from home sales, but this data set includes data from homes sold in 1999. Selling prices and list prices are in thousands of dollars. Living areas are in hundreds of square feet. Taxes are in dollars.

SELLPRIC	LISTPRICE	LIVINGAREA	ROOMS	BEDRMS	BATHRMS	AGE	ACRES	TAXES
142	160	28	10	5	3	60	0.28	3167
175	180	18	8	4	1	12	0.43	4033
129	132	13	6	3	1	41	0.33	1471
138	140	17	7	3	1	22	0.46	3204
232	240	25	8	4	3	5	2.05	3613
135	140	18	7	4	3	9	0.57	3028
150	160	20	8	4	3	18	4	3131
207	225	22	8	4	2	16	2.22	5158
271	285	30	10	5	2	30	0.53	5702
89	90	10	5	3	1	43	0.3	2054
153	157	22	8	3	3	18	0.38	4127
86.5	90	16	7	3	1	50	0.65	1445
234	238	25	8	4	2	2	1.61	2087
105.5	116	20	8	4	1	13	0.22	2818
175	180	22	8	4	2	15	2.06	3917
165	170	17	8	4	2	33	0.46	2220
166	170	23	9	4	2	37	0.27	3498
136	140	19	7	3	1	22	0.63	3607
148	160	17	7	3	2	13	0.36	3648
151	153	19	8	4	2	24	0.34	3561
180	190	24	9	4	2	10	1.55	4681
293	305	26	8	4	3	6	0.46	7088
167	170	20	9	4	2	46	0.46	3482
190	193	22	9	5	2	37	0.48	3920
184	190	21	9	5	2	27	1.3	4162
157	165	20	8	4	2	7	0.3	3785
110	115	16	8	4	1	26	0.29	3103
135	145	18	7	4	1	35	0.43	3363
567	625	64	11	4	4	4	0.85	12192
180	185	20	8	4	2	11	1	3831
183	188	17	7	3	2	16	3	3564
185	193	20	9	3	2	56	6.49	3765
152	155	17	8	4	1	33	0.7	3361
148	153	13	6	3	2	22	0.39	3950
152	159	15	7	3	1	25	0.59	3055
146	150	16	7	3	1	31	0.36	2950
170	190	24	10	3	2	33	0.57	3346
127	130	20	8	4	1	65	0.4	3334
265	270	36	10	6	3	33	1.2	5853
157	163	18	8	4	2	12	1.13	3982
128	135	17	9	4	1	25	0.52	3374
110	120	15	8	4	2	11	0.59	3119
123	130	18	8	4	2	43	0.39	3268
212	230	39	12	5	3	202	4.29	3648

145	145	18	8	4	2	44	0.22	2783
129	135	10	6	3	1	15	1	2438
143	145	21	7	4	2	10	1.2	3529
247	252	29	9	4	2	4	1.25	4626
111	120	15	8	3	1	97	1.11	3205
133	145	26	7	3	1	42	0.36	3059

OLDM&M: Data Set 14 in *Elementary Statistics* includes recent weights from a sample of M&M plain candies, but this data set includes weights from a sample collected in 1993.

RED	ORANGE	YELLOW	BROWN	BLUE	GREEN
0.87	0.903	0.906	0.932	0.838	0.911
0.933	0.92	0.978	0.86	0.875	1.002
0.952	0.861	0.926	0.919	0.87	0.902
0.908	1.009	0.868	0.914	0.956	0.93
0.911	0.971	0.876	0.914	0.968	0.949
0.908	0.898	0.968	0.904		0.89
0.913	0.942	0.921	0.93		0.902
0.983	0.897	0.893	0.871		
0.92		0.939	1.033		
0.936		0.886	0.955		
0.891		0.924	0.876		
0.924		0.91	0.856		
0.874		0.877	0.866		
0.908		0.879	0.858		
0.924		0.941	0.988		
0.897		0.879	0.936		
0.912		0.94	0.93		
0.888		0.96	0.923		
0.872		0.989	0.867		
0.898		0.9	0.965		
0.882		0.917	0.902		
		0.911	0.928		
		0.892	0.9		
		0.886	0.889		
		0.949	0.875		
		0.934	0.909		
			0.976		
			0.921		
			0.898		
			0.897		
			0.902		
			0.92		
			0.909		

OLDOLDFAITHFUL: Data Set 11 in the 10th edition of *Elementary Statistics* includes recent Old Faithful measurements, but these are from 1995. Duration times are in seconds, interval times between eruptions are in minutes, and heights are in feet.

DURATION	INTERVAL	GEYSERHT
240	86	140
237	86	154
122	62	140
267	104	140
113	62	160
258	95	140
232	79	150
105	62	150
276	94	160
248	79	155
243	86	125
241	85	136
214	86	140
114	58	155
272	89	130
227	79	125
237	83	125
238	82	139
203	84	125
270	82	140
218	78	140
226	91	135
250	89	141
245	79	140
120	57	139
267	100	110
103	62	140
270	87	135
241	70	140
239	88	135
233	82	140
238	83	139
102	56	100
271	81	105
127	74	130
275	102	135
140	61	131
264	83	135
134	73	153
268	97	155
124	67	140
270	90	150
249	84	153
237	82	120
235	81	138

228	78	135
265	89	145
120	69	130
275	98	136
241	79	150

QWERTY: Ratings of difficulty of typing each of the 52 words in the Preamble to the Constitution using the QWERTY configuration of keys (found on typical keyboards in use today) and the Dvorak configuration designed to make typing easier. Higher values correspond to words that are more difficult to type.

QWERTY	DVORAK
2	2
2	0
5	3
1	1
2	0
6	0
3	0
3	0
4	2
2	0
4	4
0	0
5	3
7	4
7	0
5	3
6	3
6	1
8	3
10	5
7	4
2	2
2	0
10	5
5	1
8	4
2	0
5	3
4	5
2	0
6	2
2	0
6	4
1	1

7	5
2	0
7	4
2	0
3	1
8	3
1	0
5	1
2	0
5	3
2	0
14	1
2	2
2	0
6	0
3	0
1	1
7	4

STOWAWAYS: Ages of stowaways on the Queen Mary, categorized by westbound crossings and eastbound crossings. The data are from the Cunard Steamship Co., Ltd.

Westbound	Eastbound
41	24
24	24
32	34
26	15
39	19
45	22
24	18
21	20
22	20
21	17
40	17
18	20
33	18
33	23
19	37
31	15
16	25
16	28
23	21
19	15
16	48
20	18
18	12
22	15
26	23

22	25
38	22
42	21
25	30
21	19
29	20
24	20
18	35
17	19
24	38
18	26
19	19
30	20
18	19
24	41
31	31
30	20
48	19
29	18
34	42
25	25
23	19
41	47
16	19
17	22
15	20
19	23
18	24
66	37
27	23
43	30
	32
	28
	32
	48
	27
	31
	22
	34
	26
	20
	22
	15
	19
	20
	18
	26
	36
	31
	35

SURVEY: Survey results from 100 statistics students. Results include gender, age, height, value of coins in possession, number of keys, number of credit cards, pulse rate (beats per minute), whether the subject exercises, whether the subject smokes, whether the subject is color blind, and handedness (right, left, ambidextrous).

SEX	AGE	HT	COINS	KEYS	CREDIT	PULSE	EXERCISE	COLOR	HAND	SMOKE
2	19	64	0	3	0	97	2	2	2	2
2	28	67.5	100	5	0	88	1	2	2	2
1	19	68	0	0	1	69	1	1	2	2
1	20	70.5	23	4	2	67	1	2	3	2
2	18	65	35	5	5	83	1	2	2	2
2	17	63	185	6	0	77	1	2	2	2
1	18	75	0	3	0	66	2	2	2	2
2	48	64	0	3	0	60	2	2	3	2
2	19	68.75	43	3	0	78	2	2	3	2
2	17	57	35	3	0	73	1	2	1	1
2	35	63	250	10	2	8	1	2	2	2
2	18	64	178	5	10	67	1	2	2	1
1	19	72	10	2	1	55	1	2	2	2
2	28	67	90	5	0	72	1	2	2	1
2	24	62.5	0	8	14	82	1	2	1	1
2	30	63	200	1	10	70	1	2	2	2
1	21	69	0	5	0	47	1	2	1	2
1	19	68	40	4	2	63	1	2	2	1
1	19	68	73	2	0	52	2	2	2	1
1	24	68	20	2	1	55	1	2	2	2
2	22	5	500	4	1	67	1	2	2	2
1	21	69	0	2	1	75	2	2	1	2
1	19	69	0	3	3	76	1	2	2	2
2	19	60	35	10	0	60	2	2	2	2
1	20	69	130	3	0	84	1	2	2	2
1	30	73	62	10	1	40	1	2	2	2
1	33	74	5	7	8	64	1	2	2	2
1	19	67	0	3	0	72	2	2	2	2
1	18	70	0	5	1	72	1	2	2	2
1	20	70	0	3	5	75	1	1	2	2
2	18	76	0	3	0	80	2	2	2	2
1	20	68	32	2	4	63	1	2	2	2
1	50	72	74	8	4	72	2	2	2	2
2	20	65	14	4	4	90	1	2	2	1
1	18	68	25	2	0	70	2	2	2	2
2	18	64	0	2	0	100	2	2	2	2
2	18	64	25	1	0	69	1	2	2	2
1	22	68	0	5	5	64	1	2	2	2
2	21	64	27	2	2	80	2	2	2	2
1	41	72	76	2	0	60	2	2	2	1
1	18	68	160	3	0	66	2	2	2	1
1	21	68	34	26	0	78	1	2	2	2
2	17	60	75	3	0	60	2	2	2	1
2	40	64	20	10	5	68	1	2	2	2

1	19	74	0	1	3	72	1	2	2	2
1	19	69	0	5	0	60	1	2	2	2
2	28	68	453	5	7	88	1	2	2	1
2	28	64	0	3	0	58	1	2	2	2
2	19	63	79	6	0	88	1	2	1	2
2	41	63	100	6	3	80	2	2	2	2
1	18	71	25	2	1	61	1	2	2	2
1	18	73	181	6	0	67	2	2	2	2
1	21	71	72	3	4	60	1	2	2	1
1	18	73	0	5	0	80	1	2	2	2
1	22	69	75	12	5	60	1	2	2	1
2	22	69	0	3	5	80	1	2	2	2
1	21	72	0	4	0	68	1	2	2	1
2	26	60	25	15	0	78	1	2	2	2
1	21	72	97	2	0	54	1	2	2	2
1	20	54	0	5	5	81	2	2	2	2
2	19	65	0	8	0	67	2	2	2	2
1	22	66	30	8	4	70	1	2	2	2
1	20	76	0	6	1	63	1	2	2	2
1	19	71	0	7	0	90	1	1	2	2
1	36	73	18	11	4	70	2	2	2	2
1	20	71	0	5	1	69	2	1	2	2
1	19	71	50	7	0	69	2	2	2	1
2	18	67.5	0	4	0	75	2	2	2	1
2	19	64	0	3	1	80	1	2	2	1
1	52	71.7	51	4	5	92	2	2	2	2
2	41	68	800	7	4	72	2	2	2	2
1	20	69	0	3	3	63	1	2	2	1
1	20	72	85	3	1	60	1	2	2	2
2	30	63	111	5	0	78	2	2	2	2
1	21	73	77	5	0	77	1	2	2	2
1	21	70	35	5	4	71	1	2	2	1
2	34	65.5	300	4	2	15	2	2	2	2
1	19	69	36	5	0	83	2	2	2	1
1	20	69	0	2	0	80	1	2	2	2
1	20	69	0	1	1	71	1	2	2	2
2	20	66	45	4	0	86	2	2	2	2
2	36	64.5	116	3	8	65	1	2	2	2
1	19	68	52	4	2	70	1	2	2	2
2	20	67	358	7	7	76	1	2	2	2
1	19	71	0	4	0	78	1	2	2	1
1	19	72	15	10	1	63	1	2	3	2
1	19	71	1	0	0	52	1	2	2	1
1	25	71	25	4	1	78	2	2	1	2
2	29	64	26	6	3	92	2	2	2	2
1	19	81	0	4	3	48	1	2	2	2
2	17	67.5	0	3	0	68	1	2	2	2
2	19	68	0	8	1	85	2	2	2	2
1	24	73	0	14	0	64	1	2	1	2
2	19	63	0	3	4	65	2	2	2	2

2	18	64	25	3	0	*	1	2	2	2
2	23	69	0	3	26	*	2	2	1	1
1	19	60	50	4	0	*	1	2	2	2
1	19	72	83	6	2	*	1	2	2	1
2	21	67	50	3	8	*	1	2	2	2
1	20	74	0	6	0	*	2	2	1	1

SYSTOLIC: The blood pressure measurements (mm Hg) are taken before and after a period consisting of 25 minutes of aerobic bicycle exercise. During the pre- and post-exercise periods, subjects were measured during a time of no stress, and a time of stress caused by an arithmetic test, and a time of stress caused by a speech test. Data are from "Sympathoadrenergic Mechanisms in Reduced Hemodynamic Stress Responses after Exercise" by Kim Brownley et al, *Medicine and Science in Sports and Exercise*, Vol. 35, No. 6.

SEX	RACE	Pre-Ex. No Stress	Pre-Ex. Math Stress	Pre-Ex. Speech Stress	Post-Ex. No Stress	Post-Ex. Math Stress	Post-Ex. Speech Stress
Female	Black	117.00	131.00	128.50	110.00	122.33	123.50
Female	Black	130.67	142.33	147.50	114.00	129.33	134.50
Female	Black	102.67	109.00	112.00	99.67	108.67	109.50
Female	Black	93.67	103.00	114.00	99.00	101.33	105.00
Female	Black	96.33	106.33	114.00	93.33	105.00	101.50
Female	Black	92.00	112.00	114.50	100.33	107.67	112.50
Male	Black	115.67	129.33	128.00	115.00	135.67	125.50
Male	Black	120.67	147.67	138.50	115.00	129.00	130.00
Male	Black	133.00	159.67	149.00	144.00	154.00	148.50
Male	Black	120.33	131.67	143.00	120.00	128.33	118.50
Male	Black	124.67	160.33	172.50	121.00	145.67	168.50
Male	Black	118.33	136.33	154.50	108.33	128.00	146.00
Female	White	119.67	143.00	141.00	115.33	131.33	124.00
Female	White	106.00	129.33	132.00	113.00	130.00	129.00
Female	White	108.33	148.00	149.50	110.33	139.33	135.00
Female	White	107.33	128.00	135.00	109.33	126.67	127.50
Female	White	117.00	134.67	135.00	125.67	127.67	131.00
Female	White	113.33	121.00	133.00	103.33	109.67	117.00
Male	White	124.33	138.00	144.50	129.00	125.33	134.50
Male	White	111.00	139.00	141.50	109.67	133.33	131.50
Male	White	99.67	123.67	130.00	114.33	124.67	128.50
Male	White	128.33	141.33	142.00	119.00	126.67	130.50
Male	White	102.00	123.00	134.50	108.00	122.00	122.50
Male	White	127.33	156.67	163.50	127.33	154.00	146.50

YEAST: The data are counts of yeast cells using a haemacytometer, and each value is the count over 1 mm^2 divided into 400 squares. The data were collected by William S. Gosset, who developed the Student *t* distribution. Gosset was an employee of the Guiness Brewery, and his contributions to statistics have origins in the brewing process, which requires yeast used for fermentation. Counts of yeast cells were important because the addition of too little yeast would result in incomplete fermentation, but too much yeast would result in beer with a bitter taste. The data are from *Student's Collected Papers*, edited by E.S. Pearson and John Wishart, Cambridge University Press, London, 1958. (Gosset published with the pseudonym of "A Student.")

2	3	7	4	4	4	3	7	8	1
4	5	2	5	5	8	6	7	4	7
2	3	9	1	1	4	7	5	10	3
2	9	2	12	6	4	6	2	3	6
4	2	5	4	5	5	4	6	6	7
5	3	11	5	5	6	4	5	1	7
4	4	2	7	9	10	5	3	3	2
4	5	4	8	4	6	2	7	6	2
4	2	7	3	3	4	1	6	3	5
8	6	6	2	4	5	6	4	2	4
5	5	4	2	4	4	8	7	6	5
6	4	6	4	5	3	6	6	5	5
2	4	4	3	4	3	5	4	5	5
3	6	4	2	2	3	7	4	3	1
4	2	2	5	6	8	7	5	2	3
4	5	6	1	7	5	5	5	3	3
7	8	4	8	6	3	9	8	5	3
6	7	2	6	6	7	4	1	3	12
7	6	4	2	5	2	5	6	3	4
5	1	5	4	2	4	5	5	7	4
4	3	4	9	4	1	8	3	11	6
2	3	3	5	7	5	8	10	4	2
7	6	3	5	6	4	9	3	3	5
6	6	5	1	3	5	6	8	3	2
5	6	5	3	5	1	5	4	7	6
6	5	7	2	5	5	7	7	7	8
2	10	6	9	5	5	6	3	4	1
1	4	2	9	4	6	6	5	8	7
8	8	5	5	4	6	6	7	7	6
2	2	6	1	4	10	4	4	4	6
6	3	4	5	3	4	4	4	3	4
2	8	5	3	5	2	2	6	7	7
7	5	1	2	5	2	3	4	5	4
2	9	5	4	4	3	6	4	3	6
4	6	4	4	9	3	7	4	5	4
5	5	1	7	7	8	1	4	1	3
3	4	2	3	6	3	4	5	3	6
2	4	2	3	5	3	1	7	4	5
4	4	6	4	4	3	4	3	4	4
2	3	7	6	4	5	4	5	4	4